Sharpe

Pocket Refere

Sharpening

Pocket Reference Book

• TECHNIQUES & EQUIPMENT •

Jim Kingshott

Guild of Master Craftsman Publications Ltd

First published 1996 by
Guild of Master Craftsman Publications Ltd,
166 High Street, Lewes,
East Sussex BN7 1XU

ISBN 1 86108 007 7

Designed by Fineline Studios

Typeface: ITC Stone Sans

Printed and bound in Great Britain by Hillman Printers (Frome) Ltd, Frome, Somerset

Contents

To my son
John

Introduction

Most craftsmen (and women) have their own ideas about sharpening tools, and hold fiercely to them, but there can be no dispute that without sharp tools it is impossible to produce anything worthwhile from wood. I therefore decided to write this book in order to pass on some of what I have picked up regarding sharpening during my time in the trade. I do not say that these are the only methods, but they are those which I consider worth knowing.

Sharpening is the most important skill that a woodworker must acquire, yet scant attention is often paid to it. Sharpening is looked upon by many as a necessary evil which wastes production time. Yet sharp tools are a pleasure to work with and make our work so much easier; blunt tools only lead to frustration. Work produced by sharp tools has a crisp, clean appearance, while blunt tools leave a dull, coarse surface. The precision of cut from a sharp tool will enable you to produce perfect joints. However, the skill of sharpening, as with other skills, is only developed by practice, so do not be disappointed when trying new methods if they do not work out too well at first.

I hope that you will gain something from this book; it should help to make your tools sharper, and consequently allow you to enjoy working wood that much more.

Please forgive the occasional use of the masculine pronoun in this book, and the use of 'craftsman' instead of that horrid word 'craftsperson'. I mean no slight to women; in all cases I refer to either sex.

CHAPTER 1

Sharpness

Without doubt, the single thing that most affects the quality of work a woodworker produces is the condition of the cutting edge on the tools. A tool that is not cutting properly affects production in a number of ways, for example:

- The tool requires more physical effort from the user.
- The tool takes the path of least resistance and is hard to control.
- The cut surface is ragged.
- The user becomes frustrated, and concentration is lost.
- The work takes longer to complete.

It is vital that tools are in prime cutting condition, and we must therefore be able to recognize sharpness, and conversely bluntness.

There is no way to measure sharpness, and the degree of sharpness required will vary with the use to which the tool is being put. For instance, the edge on a finely set smoothing plane would need to be sharper than that on an axe. The edge on the smoother would also

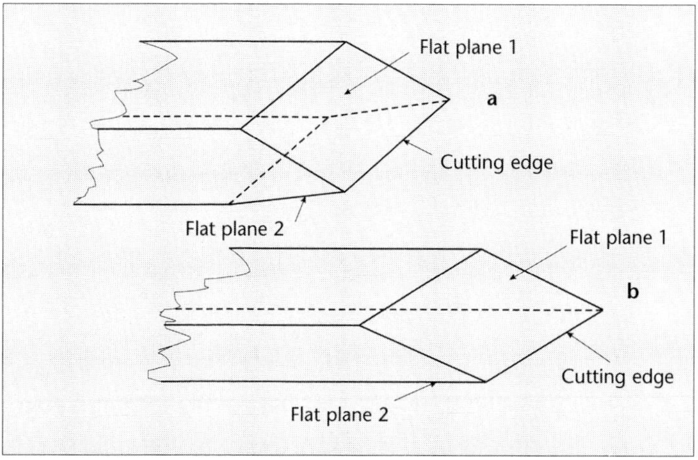

Fig 1.1 A cutting edge formed by two flat planes.

need resharpening more often than that of the axe, even if both were used on the same type of wood. When we say a tool is sharp, we mean it is *sharp enough to efficiently perform the task for which it is being used.*

If we understand exactly how a cutting edge does what we ask of it, we shall also be able to improve its efficiency. Let us look at a cutting edge on the end of a flat bar of steel. The edge is produced by two perfectly flat planes at an angle to one another. This can be seen in Fig 1.1a. On some tools one flat plane is formed by the flat face of the steel, and only one face has a bevel (Fig 1.1b). This is usually the case on chisels and plane blades.

What is Required to Produce a Cutting Edge?

In the last paragraph, I mentioned a flat bar of *steel* and two *flat planes*. While a sharp edge can be put on many different metals, only steel of a certain quality will remain sharp for a reasonable time (steel is discussed in Chapter 2). The two flat planes are produced by abrading metal away, and various tools and devices are used to accomplish this. It is important that the operative understands the technology of each tool, because the way tools cut varies in many subtle ways. Without that knowledge it is impossible to know what sort of edge the tool requires. For instance, a smoothing plane cuts with a sharp edge formed by the two flat planes previously described, but a cabinet scraper has a hooked edge that cuts in an entirely different fashion. Then there is the skill factor. This is something which can hardly be described, because skill is developed by practice.

Testing for Sharpness

Do not try and test tools for sharpness by running the ball of your thumb along the cutting edge: it is unnecessary and can be painful! Once you know what you are looking for, it is possible to see if a tool is sharp by *inspecting* the cutting edge. A blunt edge has a minute white line along its edge, known as the candle. If you take a tool that you know is blunt and inspect the edge with a magnifying glass you will see the candle. Hold the blade in good light and tip it back and

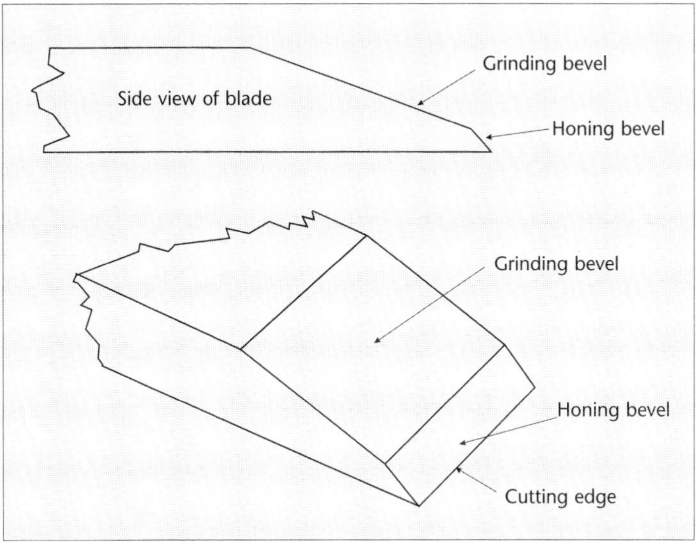

Fig 1.2 A typical cutting edge.

forth so that the light reflects off the candle. After a little practice it soon becomes possible to see even a slightly blunt edge with the naked eye, although it is a good idea to have a glass handy to minutely inspect cutting edges. This is a help when a cutting edge has to be produced for a very special purpose – for instance, the iron from a polishing plane.

Different Angles

The angle between the two flat surfaces forming the cutting edge affects both the ease with which the tool cuts and the strength of the edge. Most cutting edges have two bevels, the **grinding bevel** and the **honing bevel** (Fig 1.2). Here we are only considering the honing bevel, as this is the only bevel that affects the cutting action of the blade. A low-angle blade (Fig 1.3) enters the wood with less effort than the steep-angle blade. However, the cutting edge of the low-angle blade is thin and fragile, while the steep-angle blade has more metal behind the cutting edge and is stronger. We are thus faced with a compromise. Do we sharpen at a low angle so that the tool cuts easily, with little effort, and sharpen more often? Or do we

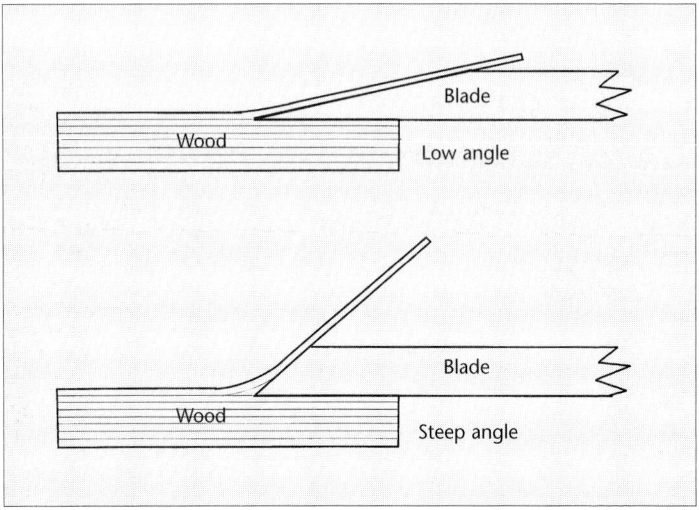

Fig 1.3 The angle of a tool entering wood. The low-angled blade cuts with less effort than the steep-angled blade.

sharpen with a steep angle and use more energy in our work and sharpen less often? In practice, we sharpen our tools to suit the task in hand. A soft wood that cuts easily and requires little effort to make a cut will not put much strain on the cutting edge, so we can have a low angle. A hard wood that requires the tool to be driven with a good deal of force will need an edge that can stand up to this robust treatment. As you can see, everything that is for us is against us. Hard wood that is difficult to cut requires the tool to be sharpened so that it requires more effort on our part. It's a hard world.

The Exception: Planes

A plane blade is pitched at an angle to the work. Thus the only angle that the wood sees is the angle at the front of the iron (Fig 1.4). Whether the angle at which the blade is sharpened has any effect other than applying a clearance angle is a contentious issue among craftsmen. However, I have found from experience that blades sharpened at a low angle cut better than those sharpened at a steep angle. When all the variables connected with the cutting action of a plane blade are considered, we realize that

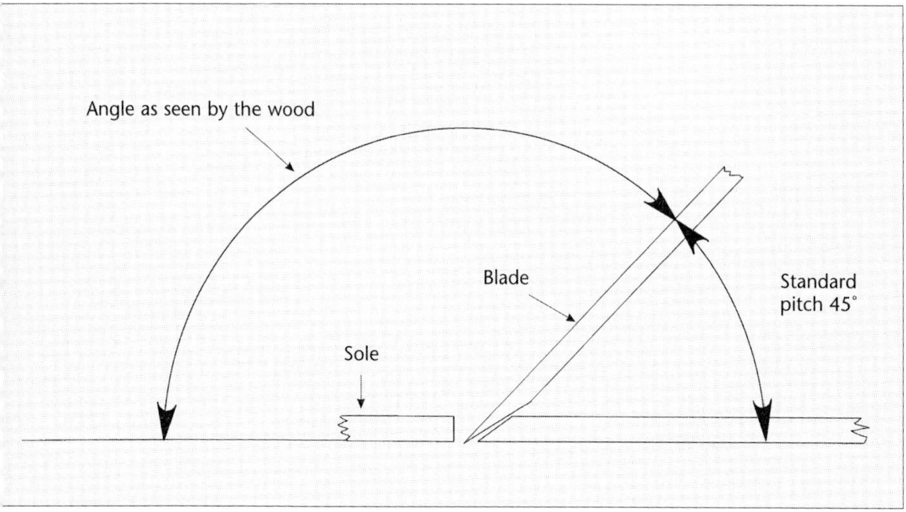

Fig 1.4 Angle of blade pitch in plane, as opposed to the sharpening angle.

there are a number of imponderable questions. Does the plane blade deflect as it is pushed into the wood, and if so what effect does this have on the cutting action? We know that the thin blade in the Bailey pattern plane deflects when it meets a hard knot, because a chatter is induced. How does the tension applied to the blade by the back iron bolt affect the working, if at all? Sharpening is not as straightforward as it might at first seem. Planes are discussed fully in Chapter 8.

Wear and Tear

As sharpening is performed by abrading metal from the tool, the life of the tool is reduced every time it is sharpened. Added to this, time spent in sharpening is lost production time, so we do not want to sharpen more often than is necessary.

Tools should be stored in a way that protects their cutting edge. When a tool is placed down on the bench it should be placed so that its edge is protected from any grit on the bench, or from being knocked by another tool. I shall explain ways of achieving this as I discuss the sharpening of each tool.

CHAPTER 2

Metallurgy

It may seem difficult to understand why a book about woodwork should need a chapter describing metal. However, an important part of most of our tools is made from steel. In most cases we have no say in the choice or heat treatment of this material, but if something goes wrong we need to be able to diagnose the problem, and if possible put it right. When buying flat-ground tool steel from which to make blades and cutters for hand tools or machines, we need to understand the specification so that we can make the right choice. As most of the woodworking processes involve cutting it is essential that we fully understand the material from which cutting tools are made.

Some Definitions

In order to fully understand what follows, some terms used to describe the characteristics of steel need to be defined.

- *Brittleness.* The property of breaking with very little deformation.
- *Fusibility.* The ability of a metal to be easily liquefied by heat.
- *Hardness.* The ability of a material to withstand scratching, wear and abrasion, and its power to resist penetration.
- *Malleability.* The ability of a material to have its shape permanently changed by hammering, rolling, or pressing, without fracture.
- *Tensile strength.* A measure of a material's resistance to a load tending to pull it apart.
- *Toughness.* The ability of a material to withstand sudden heavy loading, without fracture.

The Process

Steel is made from cast iron, which is produced in a blast furnace. The furnace is loaded from the top with iron ore, coke and limestone. Hot air is blown in at the bottom of the furnace causing the coke to burn and raise the temperature to 140°C. Metallic pig iron is drawn off from the bottom of the furnace and contains 3–4% carbon and various impurities. This process is known as smelting.

The pig iron is again melted together with coke and limestone in a furnace called a cupola. Grey cast iron is tapped from the base of the cupola. This metal typically contains:

93.5%	Iron	0.1%	Sulphur
3.5%	Carbon	0.4%	Phosphorus
2.0%	Silicon	0.5%	Manganese

The fundamental difference between cast iron and steel is the carbon content. To make steel it is necessary to reduce the carbon content and to remove other impurities. This is done by oxidation (i.e. causing them to combine with oxygen). There are three different processes which are used to achieve this: the open hearth process; the Bessemer converter process and the electric furnace process.

Classification

Types of steel can be broadly classified under two headings, as plain carbon steel or alloy steel.

Plain carbon steel can be broken down into four groups:

- Low carbon steel 0.1 – 0.15% carbon
- Mild steel 0.15 – 0.3% carbon
- Medium carbon steels 0.3 – 0.7% carbon
- High carbon steel 0.7 – 1.7% carbon

As the carbon content of the steel is increased the hardness and tensile strength is increased. This is accompanied by a decrease in toughness. As woodworkers our main interest is in high carbon steel, the grade which will best take and maintain a sharp edge.

Most mass-produced woodworking cutting tools are made from alloy steel. This is plain carbon steel which has had other elements added to change its character. Some of the elements which are added, and in which woodworkers may be interested are:

- *Chromium*. This increases hardness, strength and resistance to corrosion.
- *Cobalt*. This increases hardness, and helps towards maintaining hardness at high temperatures, but decreases toughness.

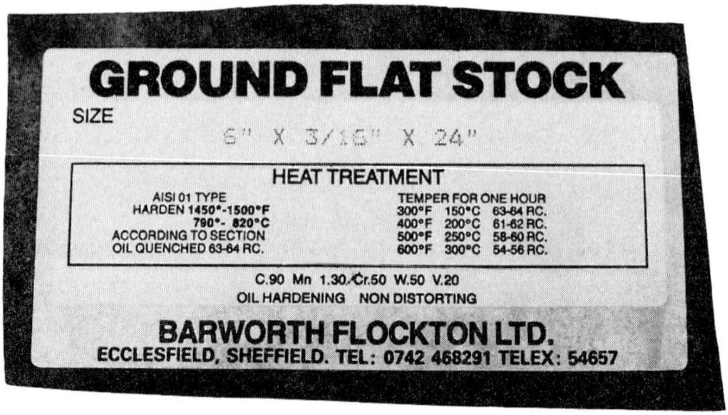

Fig 2.1 Label from a packet of steel used to make machine cutters.

- *Molybdenum.* This increases tensile strength and toughness.
- *Manganese.* This increases toughness and tensile strength.
- *Nickel.* This increases tensile strength, hardness, toughness and ductility.
- *Silicon.* This strengthens the steel.
- *Tungsten.* This increases toughness at high temperatures and improves corrosion resistance.
- *Vanadium.* This increases toughness and hardness.

Is all this information about steel necessary? Yes, because the material which we buy to make shaped machine cutters comes in a wide variety of sizes and specifications. For instance, Fig 2.1 is the label from a packet I am currently using. The specification is the letters and numbers above the words 'OIL HARDENING NON DISTORTING'. C.90 indicates 0.9% carbon, Mn.1.30 indicates 1.30% manganese, Cr.50 indicates 0.5% chromium, W.50 indicates 0.5% tungsten and V.20 indicates 0.2% vanadium. I know that this is a good material but, having tried to make a hand plane blade from it, I know that it does not produce the characteristics I need for that purpose. I prefer a plain high carbon steel: all the elements that have been alloyed in this specification might make a tough material, but it will not hold the super-sharp edge I require.

Heat Treatment

The character of steel can be changed by heat treating it. When carbon steel is heated at a uniform rate, its temperature also rises uniformly until it reaches 700°C. At this point the temperature remains constant for a short time, and then rises slowly to 800°C. Then it continues to rise again at the original rate. The point at which the temperature remains stable is known as the **decalescence** point. As the metal cools the reverse happens. The temperature falls uniformly until it reaches 800°C when it slows down. At 700°C it stops briefly before continuing at the original rate. The point at which the pause occurs during cooling is known as the **recalescence** point. The point at which decalescence and recalescence occur is known as the lower critical point. The upper critical point varies from 700°C for high carbon content steel to 900°C for low carbon content steel. As steel is heated its internal structure begins to change at the lower critical point and continues to change until the upper critical point is reached. If the steel, is allowed to cool at a natural rate the structure returns to its preheated state. However, if the steel is plunged into cold water the structure remains unchanged. High carbon steel treated in this way becomes extremely hard. Steel hardened in this way is too brittle for our purpose and requires further treatment known as tempering. This entails heating the metal to a temperature below the lower critical point and again quenching it in water. The temperature to which the steel is heated for tempering effects the ultimate hardness.

Hardness Testing

If you look at Fig 2.1 you will notice the details in the box headed HEAT TREATMENT and also the words OIL HARDENING, below the box – various liquids are used for cooling the metal when hardening and tempering. In the table headed TEMPER FOR ONE HOUR there are figures followed by the letters RC, which stands for 'Rockwell C'. This is a method of describing the hardness of metal. There are numerous ways of testing and grading the hardness of material, and Rockwell is only one of them (Table 2.1). Most methods involve pushing some device into the metal, using a predetermined load. The depth of penetration is accurately measured, and the shallower the penetration the harder the material. Most tool manufacturers give the hardness of their blades in Rockwell C. The 'C' stands for the penetrate, which is made from a Brazilian diamond termed a 'Conical Brale'. The diamond is ground and polished very accurately to a cone of 120° angle and has a mechanical lapped spherical point of microscopic but exact radius.

We are thus able to specify and measure the material we intend to sharpen very accurately. Marples randomly test chisels as they leave the heat treatment room and maintain the hardness between 58° and 61° Rockwell C. The harder the tool the longer the edge lasts, but hardness is proportional to brittleness – a very hard blade chips easily. We therefore have to compromise between hardness and brittleness. Modern alloy steels seem to be best at 61° Rockwell C, though some of the older tools made from high carbon steel can be taken as far as 65° Rockwell C. Hand-made Japanese chisels are also hardened to 65° Rockwell.

A tool which is soft and does not hold an edge can be taken to an engineer for heat treatment, and we can tell him the degree to which we want it hardened. Most engineering textbooks state that woodworking tools need hardening to 58°, but this is too soft. If I have a tool heat treated I ask for 61°, if this proves brittle I reject the tool. A soft tool that will not keep its edge for a reasonable time is of no use.

As you use your tools and become experienced, you will find that some tools work better than others. You will begin to know the characteristics which are to be desired. The recognition of various characteristics of steel will be recognized; just as a wine connoisseur recognizes a fine vintage, you will recognize a fine blade. You will know what you require and be able to choose it when given a selection to pick from.

Brinell			Vickers	Rockwell 'C'	
Diam. mm	Hardness No	Calculated Tonnage	Hardness No	120° diamond cone	Scleroscope
2.20	782	171	1170	70	106
2.25	744	162	1050	68	100
2.30	713	155	935	66	95
2.35	683	149	865	64	91
2.40	652	142	802	62	87
2.45	627	136	756	60	84
2.50	600	131	708	58	81
2.55	578	126	670	57	78
2.60	555	121	634	55	75
2.65	532	116	598	53	72
2.70	512	112	570	52	70
2.75	495	108	545	50	67
2.80	477	104	521	49	65
2.85	460	100	500	47	63
2.90	444	97	480	46	61
2.95	430	94	462	45	59

Table 2.1 Conversion table of hardness scales.

CHAPTER 3

The Sharpening Process

Two Flat Planes

I described in Chapter 1 how most cutting edges on woodworking tools are formed by two flat planes meeting, so the process of sharpening is forming these two flat planes. This requires the removal of metal from the surface of the planes. It is impossible to cut hardened steel; it has to be abraded, that is, the metal is scratched or worn away. A very hard material that consists of sharp grains bonded together is used for this purpose, and the size of the grains affects the speed at which metal is removed. The grain size also affects the surface of the metal being abraded. Large grains make deep, coarse scratches, and is not conducive to obtaining a sharp edge. The grooves in the surface of the toothing plane iron (Fig 3.1) cause the

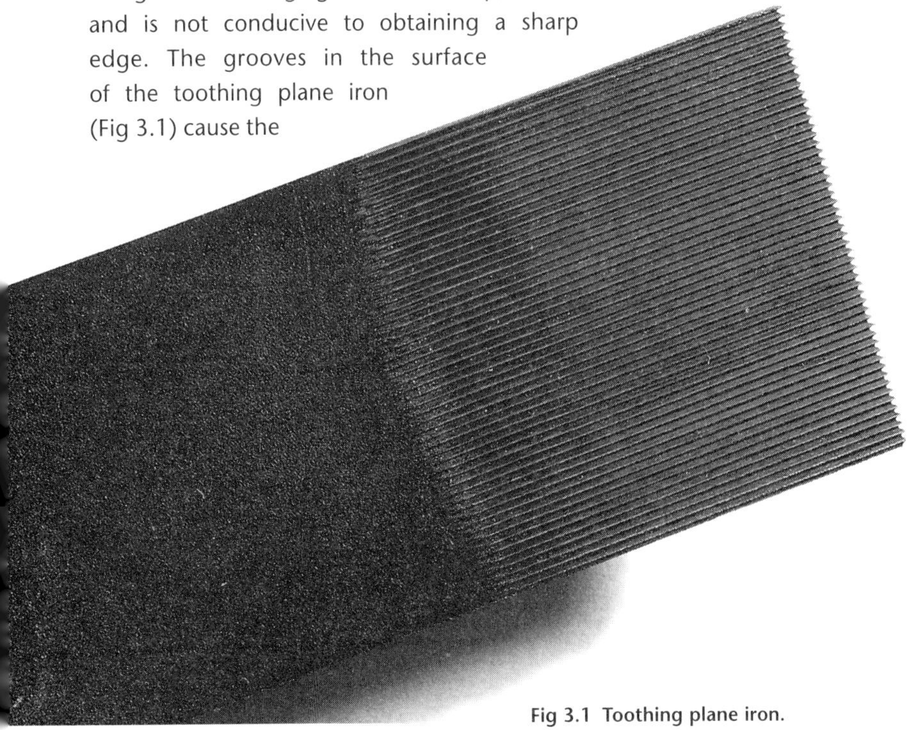

Fig 3.1 Toothing plane iron.

toothed cutting edge. This is fine when we require a serrated edge, but in most cases it is the last thing required. The scratches left by the grains of the abrading material leave a serrated edge, and the depth of the serrations depends on the depth of the scratches. Therefore, the final sharpness of the edge is proportional to the size of the grains in the sharpening material. Coarse grains cut fast but do not produce a sharp edge; fine grains take a long time to remove metal but do produce a sharp edge. Time spent on sharpening is non-productive, so we need a system that, while giving us a very sharp edge, takes the minimum of time. Most sharpening processes are also messy, and can involve oil or water. Metal removed from the tool, though in small particles, must be kept away from our work, so it is best to have somewhere away from the bench as a sharpening station. All the things needed to sharpen the tools can be stored there, ready for use.

There are various methods of abrading the metal. If a lot of material has to be removed a machine is employed. This process is known as grinding. Small amounts of material are removed by rubbing the tool on a block of abrasive, or rubbing the tool with the abrasive. This is called honing. To put the final polish on the cutting edge, fine abrasive embedded in wax is used to dress the surface of leather on which the tool is rubbed. This is called stropping. These processes are dealt with in detail in the chapters devoted to them, but before using any of them it is important that you fully understand the overall sharpening process.

Friction and Heat

All sharpening processes involve either rubbing the tool on an abrasive, or rubbing an abrasive on the tool. The friction between the moving surfaces causes heat. It is possible to spoil the tool by subjecting it to the heat caused by friction, which is one of the reasons that a lubricant or cooling agent is used when sharpening. A high-speed grinding machine used dry can bring a tool to red heat in a matter of seconds. However, the liquid has a second and important function – it floats away the metal particles removed from the tool. These particles, as small as they are, can clog the surface of the abrading material.

Both natural and man-made materials are used as abrasives. Some natural stones are quarried and cut to suitable dimensions but, as the material is extremely hard, the cutting and truing process is expensive. Man-made abrasive is as good and costs less. Some natural stone is pulverized and bonded into blocks to make sharpening stones. The term 'stone' is applied to all blocks of abrasive whether they are natural or man-made. There are four main types of abrasive grains used to make sharpening stones and grinding wheels: aluminium oxide, silicon carbide, CBN (cubic boron nitride) and diamond. Abrasive grains are broadly categorized into four main groups: very fine, fine, medium and coarse. However, this is not very scientific, and a much better way of classifying the grit size is to pass it through a sieve with a mesh of a known size, the mesh being classified by the number of wires to the linear inch, which can vary from 12 to 8,000. Only the Japanese make stones as fine as 8,000 grit.

Two Bevels

When we rub one of the flat surfaces which form the cutting edge on the stone, the size of the flat surface affects the time it takes to abrade the required amount of metal away. If we can reduce the size of the surface, we thus reduce the time taken to sharpen the tool, which is why many tools are sharpened with a double angle. The first bevel is formed on a grinding machine, which removes metal quickly with little effort on our part. The surface left by the grinder is too coarse to form a cutting edge, so a second and steeper bevel is formed along the cutting edge by honing. The honing process is carried out on at least two stones: first a medium and then a fine. The fine stone removes the deep scratches left by the medium stone, which has removed the even deeper scratches made by the grinding wheel. If the tool is to be used for delicate work where a super-sharp edge is required, it will probably be stropped on dressed leather, which removes the scratches made by the fine stone. The sharpening process is therefore just abrading metal away using successively finer grades of abrasive. What we are trying to achieve on the surfaces that form the cutting edge is a smooth, shiny finish – the better the shine the sharper the edge. The sharpening process becomes more complex when the tool has a shaped cutting edge. Moulding plane blades and spindle moulder (called a shaper in the USA) cutters require shaped grinding wheels and honing stones. This also applies to gouges and similar tools.

A comprehensive set of sharpening tools is required before one is able to produce any woodwork at all, and one of the problems with acquiring the right items with which to sharpen the tools is the vast range available. For instance, take a simple honing stone. The following are available, without even thinking about the grit size: silicon carbide, aluminium oxide, diamond, ceramic and Japanese water stone, plus a number of natural stones. It is impossible to say that one is better than the other. Taking just two stones, the Japanese stone cuts fast and imparts a fine finish for its grade, but wears quickly and needs constant attention if it is to remain true. Diamond that is plated on to steel remains very flat even after much use, but it leaves scratches in the surface of the tools being honed. Neither of these tools can be directly compared with the other; each has advantages and disadvantages, and we have to decide how they will affect our individual requirements. You have to bear in mind that irregular, pointed grains scratch more than regular, smoother grains of the same size.

Experimentation

Sharpening and the tools used to achieve a fine cutting edge is a most controversial subject. In this book I shall describe what I have found best for my own particular purpose. You must experiment and try as many different things as possible. For instance, I have completely changed my method of sharpening in recent years. The introduction of the Japanese water stone into this country about 20 years ago was a revelation to me. I found that a superb cutting edge could be obtained in about half the time I previously spent. Then the diamond surface came along. To have a stone that cut extremely fast and remained flat was a necessity, so now I use both the ancient Japanese system and the latest diamond surface.

CHAPTER 4

Grinding

Electric power has changed the way woodworkers regard grinding. Not so many years ago the grinding wheel was turned by man power. How different things are today, when all we have to do is press a button, and even the most humble workshop has a power grinder of some sort.

There are many different designs of grinders, but they can all be divided into two groups: **wet grinders** and **dry grinders**.

The titles of these categories describe the division well. The problem with power grinding is the heat generated at the tip of the tool being ground. The old hand-turned grind stones were made of sandstone, and the lower half of the wheel was immersed in a trough of water. This worked fine, as the water clinging to the surface of the rotating wheel cooled the tool. With the introduction of power, and the ever-present quest to save time, the wheel was speeded up. Water was flung from the surface by centrifugal force, often over the operator. Some workshops turned to the high-speed dry grinding machines (bench grinders) used by the engineering trade. Because these machines are simple and easy to manufacture they cost less and are bought by many beginners – who immediately start to ruin their tools by overheating them on the machine. Without doubt, the liquid-cooled wheel is much to be preferred. Unfortunately, once we introduce liquid into the process we complicate things. The wheel has to turn much slower, so some form of gearing is needed. The liquid has to be contained, and recovered in some way during use. The cost of a wet grinder is thus always more than a comparable dry machine, and in most cases the wet grinder takes longer to perform the same task. However, it is very difficult to spoil a tool when grinding it wet, but it is difficult not to spoil it on a dry machine. Extreme care must be taken when using a dry machine, and the tool must be constantly cooled in water. One moment of relaxed concentration and another tool has lost its temper. This overheating of the steel is referred to in the trade as 'burning the steel'.

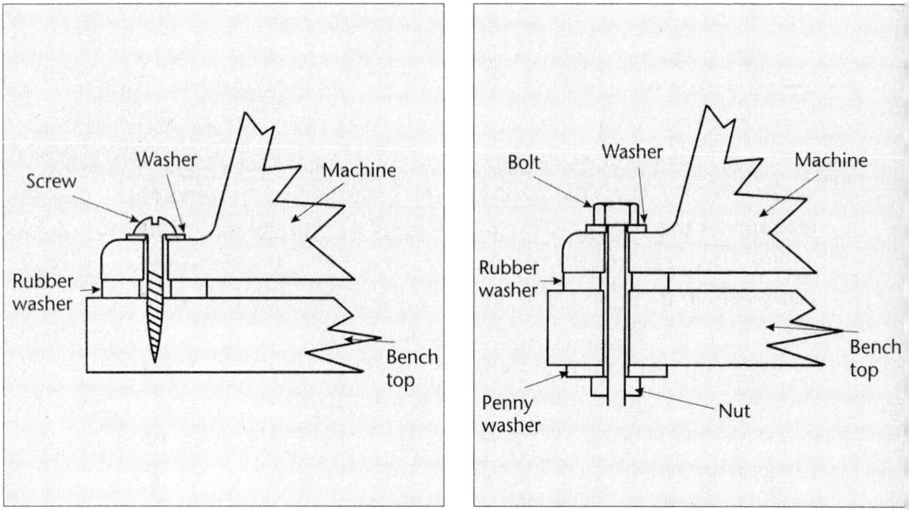

Fig 4.1 Methods of mounting a grinding machine.

There is another marked difference between machines. Most are designed so that the tool is ground on the periphery of the wheel. This imparts a hollow grind to the tool, the hollow being determined by the circumference of the wheel. A smaller number of machines are made so that the tool is ground on the side of the wheel, so the ground surface is flat. Neither method has an advantage over the other, it is a matter of personal choice.

Whatever the machine, it is essential that it is fixed firmly to the bench so that any slight movement under working pressure is avoided (Fig 4.1). Ideally, the machine should be mounted on a very stable stand which puts the grinding wheel at the most satisfactory working height.

Safety

Certain safety precautions must be taken when using grinding machines. An important point is the fragility of the wheel. Most wheels are ceramic and can be easily cracked. If a 6in wheel breaks up while revolving at 3,000 rpm it will throw pieces of broken stone about the workshop with considerable force. Wheels that are made to cut on their circumference should not be used to grind tools flat on their side. Special wheels are made for this purpose.

Safety goggles should always be worn when grinding. Goggles are better than spectacles, as the dust from the wheel is in the air and can still get into the eyes if safety glasses are worn. The transparent guards on the machine are spark guards, not eye protectors. The abrasive dust released into the air when using a dry grinder is injurious to the lungs, so always wear a dust mask. Loose clothing and jewellery can become entangled in revolving machines – don't wear them in the workshop.

The Grinding Wheel

A number of things affect the cutting characteristics of a grinding wheel, which is essentially made of thousands of small cutting tools bonded together. These tools can be made from a variety of materials. They can be large or small. They can be packed tightly together or spaced out. They can be bonded very tightly to their fellows, or only loosely held so that they can easily be dislodged. By permutating these variables you will see there are many types of wheel. Let us examine how each of these different variables affect the working characteristics of the wheel.

The larger the grains of abrasive material the faster the wheel cuts, but it imparts a poor finish. The surprising thing is that the coarse grains, although cutting faster, develop less heat than the finer grains. The grains on the surface of the wheel which impact on to the tool being ground are constantly breaking up. Every time a grain breaks away or is fractured a new minute cutting edge is exposed. Thus the material used to bond the grains together affects the speed at which the cutting surface renews itself: this is known as the hardness of the wheel.

The distance between the grains is called the density. A high-density wheel gives a better finish but is inclined to clog faster than a low-density wheel. Density is controlled by a filling material. This can be sawdust or a similar substance; when the wheel is vitrified the filling is burnt away, leaving small voids between the abrasive grains.

Several abrasive materials are used to make grinding wheels. The two most commonly met with are aluminium oxide and silicon carbide. Aluminium oxide is a hard, crystalline substance made by heating bauxite in an electric arc furnace. Silicon carbide is an artificial abrasive made by heating a mixture of sand, coke, sawdust and salt in a resistance furnace. Unfortunately, these materials are often given trade names, which can be confusing: silicon carbide is marketed as Carborundum and Crystolon by different companies, while aluminium oxide is sold under the names of Aloxide and Alundum.

There are five main bonding agents, the most important being vitrified ceramic. The others which you may occasionally meet are phenolic resin, rubber, shellac and metal.

In order that we may know which of these many variables are in the stone we buy, or so that we may specify the wheel we require, the manufacturers use a standard code to identify the characteristics of the wheels.

Hardness is graded from very soft to very hard using the letters of the alphabet (Table 4.1). The size of the abrasive grains is given by the mesh size (mesh size is described in Chapter 3) and are categorized in Table 4.2. Reference to Fig 4.2 will help to make things clear.

Table 4.1 Alphabetical classification of grinding wheel hardness.

Very soft	Soft to medium	Medium to hard	Hard	Very hard
A	E	M	U	V
B	F	N		W
C	G	O		X
D	H	P		Y
	I	Q		Z
	J	R		
	K	S		
	L	T		

Coarse	Medium	Fine	Very fine
12	30	70	150
14	36	80	180
16	46	90	200
20	60	100	240
24		120	

Table 4.2 Numerical classification of grit size in grinding wheels.

To dry grind most woodworking tools made from high carbon steel and hardened between Rockwell C 58° and 62°, we need an aluminium oxide (grey) wheel of hardness N, O, or P. Two wheels would normally be fitted, one either end of the grinding spindle, a medium wheel of around 36 grit and a fine around 100 grit. These would be vitrified bonded.

Turners using tools made from high-speed steel need soft stones, from F to K, made from aluminium oxide (pink or white) in the same grit sizes.

Tungsten carbide used on many machine cutters cannot be ground with aluminium oxide, however, a silicon carbide

Abrasive Type
A Alumina
C Silicon Carbide
11A Bauxilite
12A Special
13A Bauxilite
14A
41A Pink
47A Semi-friable
51A Mixture: Bauxilite and White Bauxilite
58A Special Bauxilite for control wheels
WA White Bauxilite
63A Mixture:
64A Zirconia Alumina and Bauxilite
AC Mixture: Bauxilite and Unirundum
BC Black Unirundum
DC Green Unirundum
GC Light Green Unirundum

Abrasive Size
Coarse
8
10
12
14
16
20
24
Medium
30
36
46
60
Fine
70
80
90
100
120
150
180
220
240
280
320
400
500
600

Grade
A
B Very
C Soft
D
E
F
G
H Soft to
I Medium
J
K
L
M
N
O Medium
P to Hard
Q
R
S
T Hard
U
V
W Very
X Hard
Y
Z

Density
Close
1
2
3
4
5
6
7
8
9
10
11
12
13
14
15
16
17
18
19
20
21
22
23
24
Open

Bond
Vitrified
V
Resinoid
B
Fabric-reinforced Resinoid
BF
Rubber
R
Fabric-reinforced Rubber
RF
Shellac
S

Special Code
Special manufacturing information, technical details and special features. This code always consists of four letters

Fig 4.2 Grinding wheel codes.

(green) wheel is required. Beware of grinding tungsten-tipped tools, as the heat generated at the grinding surface has been known to melt the brazing which joins the tungsten to the steel part of the tool.

Machines for wet grinding woodworking tools are supplied fitted with a suitable stone for the coolant used.

Mounting a Wheel

Wheels used on high-speed dry grinding machines need particular attention for two reasons – safety and balance. It is essential that the wheel is not cracked. A crack in the wheel is almost impossible to see, but it can easily be detected if you 'ring' the wheel. This is done by suspending the wheel and tapping it gently with a hard object – a chisel or screwdriver handle is ideal. A sound wheel emits a clear ringing sound, while a cracked wheel emits a dull sound which is

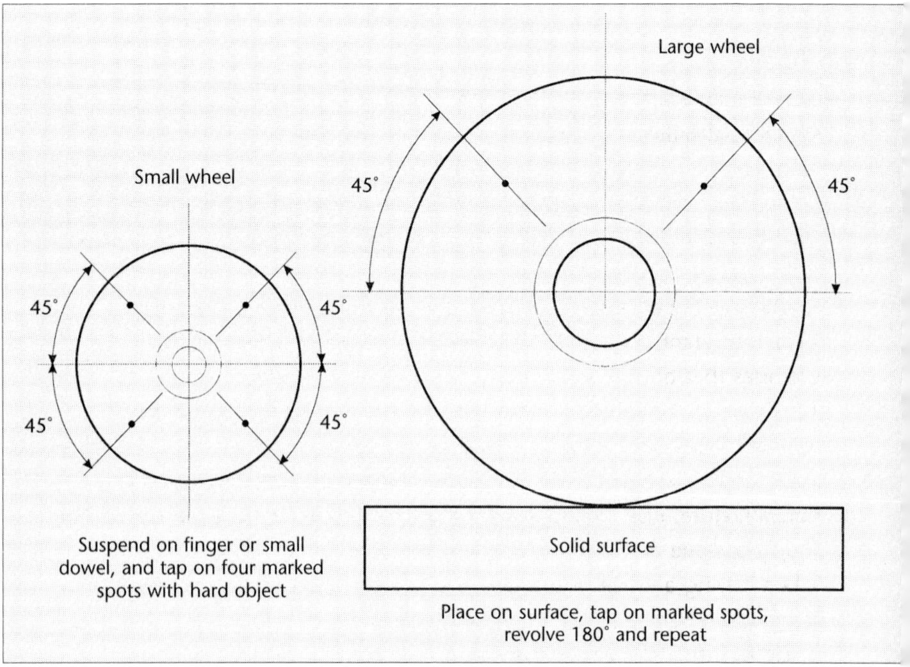

Fig 4.3 Tap testing a grinding wheel.

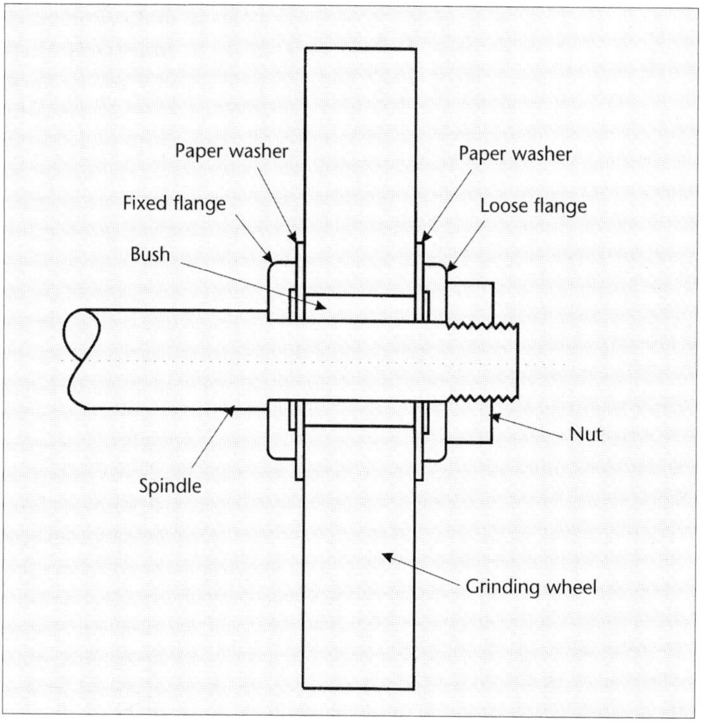

Fig 4.4 Section through a correctly mounted grinding wheel.

better described as a 'bong' than a ring. New machines usually have the wheels already mounted. They should be removed and crack tested before use (Fig 4.3).

The way the wheel is secured on the machine spindle is important – so important, in fact, that there are regulations for industrial premises that only allow specially trained staff to perform this task. The bush at the centre of the wheel must be a good fit on the spindle. Older wheels have a lead bush cast in the stone, but in recent years a removable plastic bush has been used. Distributors do not, therefore, have to stock stones with different size bushes, but supply a stone and a pair of separate bushes of the required size. When buying a wheel you need to specify the size of the machine spindle to ensure you have the correct bushes.

Either side of the wheel there needs to be a thick paper washer, a very important item. Some wheels come with them attached, in

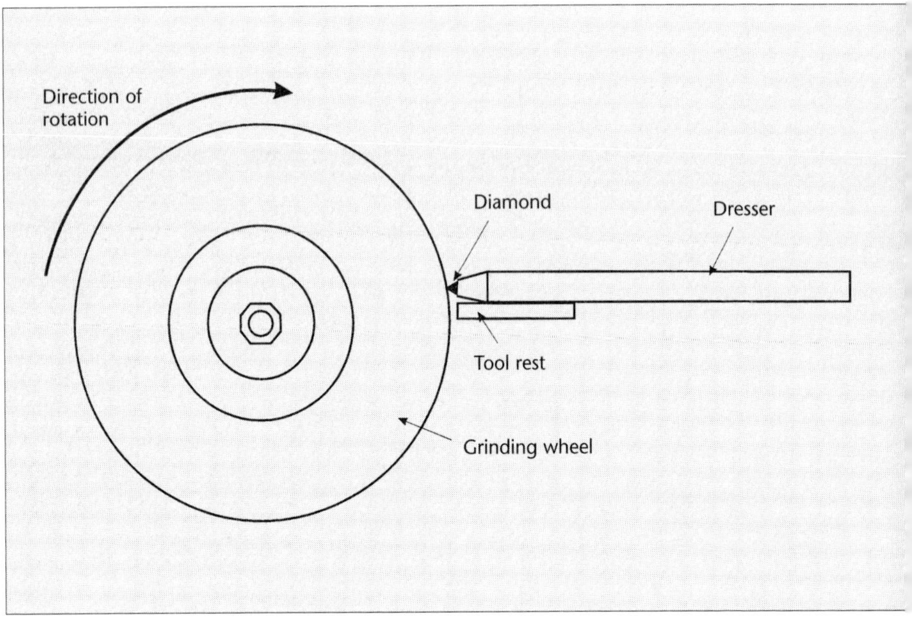

Fig 4.5 Dressing a grinding wheel with a diamond point.

which case the manufacturer prints the wheel's specification on them. If the wheel does not have paper washers a pair must be made. These washers have a dual purpose: they distribute the pressure of the clamping flange, and grip the surface of the wheel. The flanges are machined with a recessed face so that they only grip the paper close to their circumference (Fig 4.4). If the removable flange is lost or misplaced do not use a plain washer, as this will damage the wheel.

The threads on the machine spindle are cut so that the nut tightens in the reverse direction to that in which the spindle turns under power. This is so the nut does not come loose when the machine is being used. One side of a double-ended grinder therefore has a left-hand thread, an important thing to remember when removing a wheel. The clamping nut should only be tightened sufficiently to grip the wheel – on no account should it be overtightened.

As the machine revolves at high speed any out-of-balance forces will cause vibration, which will affect grinding performance. Severe vibration can be a safety hazard, as extreme forces can cause the

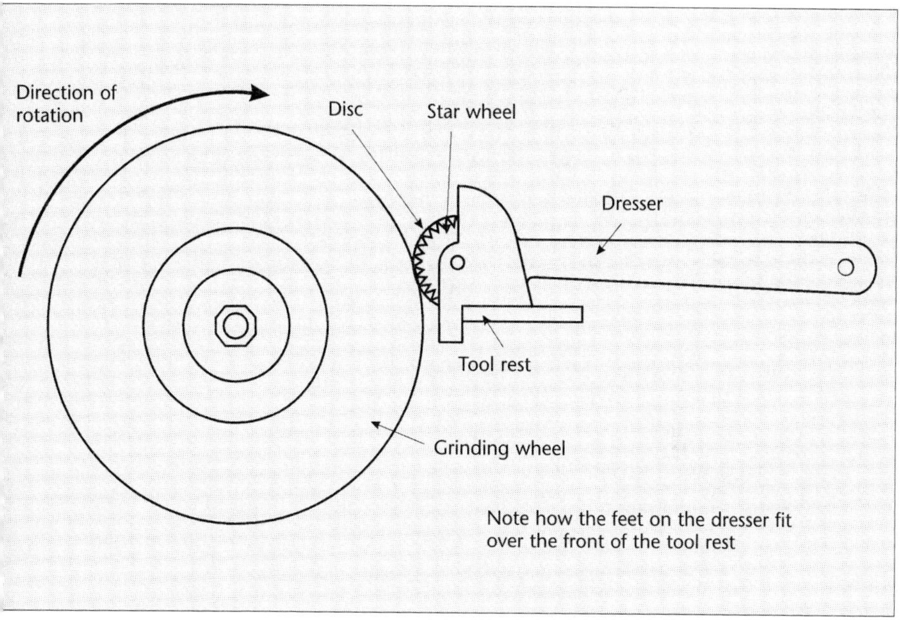

Fig 4.6 Dressing a grinding wheel with a star wheel dresser.

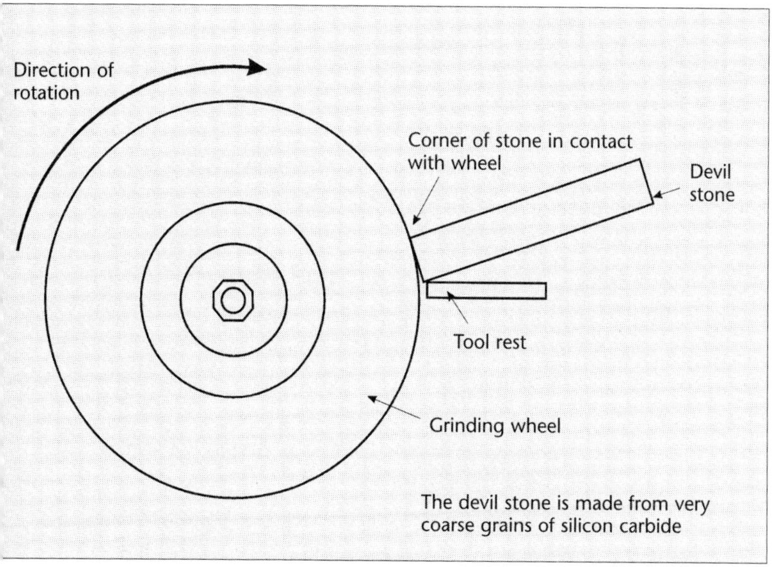

Fig 4.7 Dressing a grinding wheel with a devil stone.

wheel to shatter. The wheel is balanced by truing the surface. Material has to be removed from the wheel with a special tool, and a number of devices are used in this process. The three most suitable for the small workshop are the single-point diamond stick (Fig 4.5), the star wheel (Fig 4.6) and the devil stone (Fig 4.7). As material from the wheel is cut it forms a fine dust, so a dust mask must be worn. If the wheel is badly out of balance the sides may have to be dressed. Treat the sides with caution, and do not use undue force.

Tool Rests and Clamps

It is impossible to hold a tool against the revolving wheel and grind it accurately without some form of tool rest. Some machines come with tool clamps which present the tool being ground to the wheel at a predetermined angle. With a little ingenuity it is possible to make a suitable tool rest from wood (Fig 4.8).

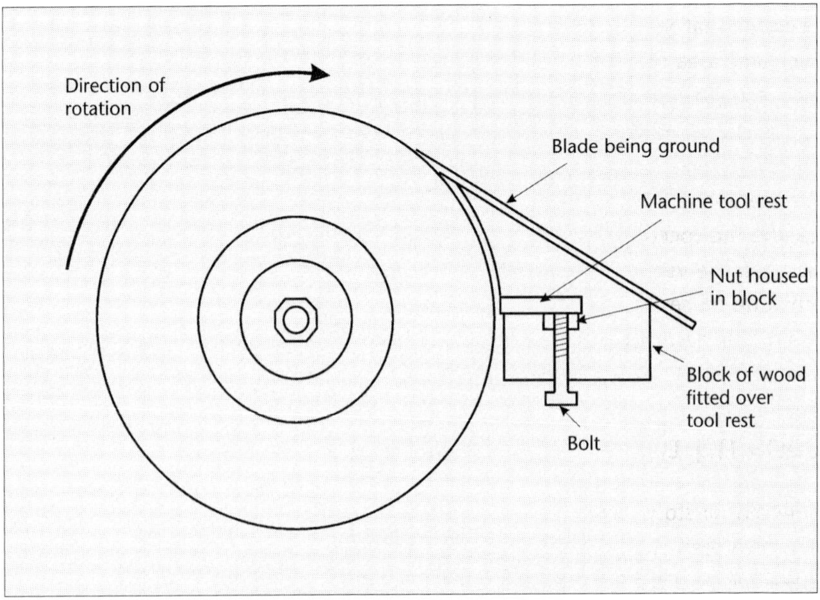

Fig 4.8 Wooden tool rest fitted to bench grinder.

CHAPTER 5

Honing

Old Stones

Almost any flat surface that is capable of abrading metal has been used at some time for honing, and a good sharpening stone has always been prized. sold stones, hidden in sheds and drawers for years, eventually come on to the secondhand market. Most of these stones will be of some use in the workshop. Razor hones are a particular example. These are narrow stones about 1in (25mm) wide and 9in (230mm) long. These stones, usually referred to as 'Turkey stone', were quarried in Asia Minor and exported to France where they were cut and finished before being exported all over the world.

Recognition

Because of the different natural and man-made stones available it is important that you are able to recognize them. You also need to have some idea of the cutting ability of a stone before buying it. A nice clean new stone presents us with little difficulty, but a stone encrusted with dried muck or contaminated with thick oil is a different matter. Regardless of all else, the most important characteristic is the cut of the stone, which is the term used to describe the speed at which the stone will remove metal. To judge this, drag the very tip of your thumb nail along the stone. Try this technique on several stones of which you know the character. The feeling from each stone is quite different. After a little experience you will soon be able to accurately judge the cut of a stone in this way.

Cooking the Stone

Some old oil stones are clogged up with oil and metal particles. I have even seen stones that have had linseed oil put on them. The linseed has oxidized and the stone has completely lost its cut. There is a way these stones can have their pores cleaned. Take an old

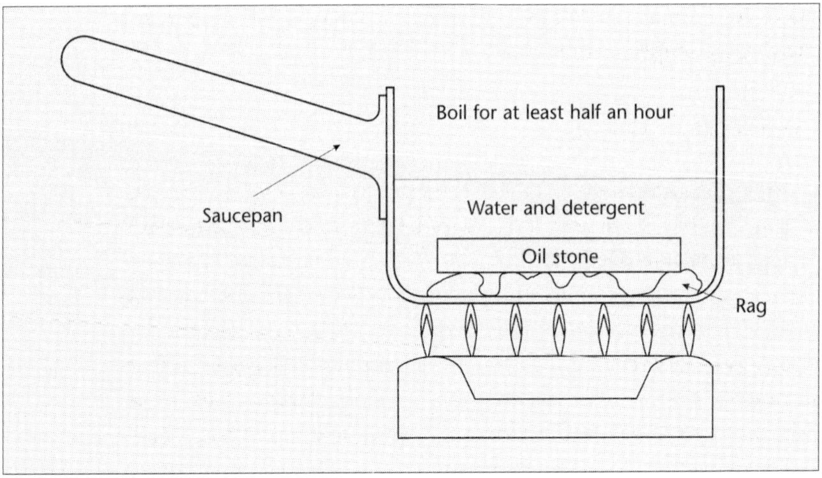

Fig 5.1 Cleaning a clogged-up oil stone.

saucepan or some such suitable receptacle (an old paint tin will do). The stone should be able to lie flat on the bottom. Put the stone in to the saucepan on some rag, just sufficient to keep the stone off the bottom of the saucepan. Half-fill the saucepan with water, add some detergent, and boil it, and keep the water around boiling point for at least half an hour (Fig 5.1). The heat will make the oil runny. The stone expands, rejecting the oil which then floats to the top of the water. A stone in very poor condition may need treating a couple of times. Do not try to cool the hot stone; let it cool down naturally, or it may crack.

Having cleaned the stone it needs to be flattened, which can be done in several ways. The fastest method is to rub it with a mixture of sand and water on a flat surface (a concrete pavement slab is useful). I use a piece of old thick plate glass and Carborundum grit, which seems less severe and more accurate. A stone flattened in this way exposes a new cutting surface, which cuts as well as when the stone was new.

Stones need to be kept in good condition, and each stone should really be kept in a fitted box. These are usually made from a solid piece of wood that has the stone housed into it. Stones are bedded into the box on plaster of Paris (Fig 5.2). The size of the stone affects its usefulness. Large bench stones are best, particularly for honing plane irons. Small slip stones are needed for gouges and other tools that have a shaped cutting edge.

Natural Stones

Our planet is composed mostly of rock, so it is surprising that so little of it is suitable for sharpening. Listed below are those stones most often available.

Arkansas

This is the best-known natural stone currently available. It is a novaculite, quarried at Hot Springs in the Ouchita Mountains in the USA. There are three distinct types of Arkansas stone: hard black, hard white and soft white. There was once a fourth variety, a translucent hard white, sometimes called a 'lily white'. This was a superb finishing stone, but unfortunately it is now only available in very small pieces. The black is a very fine grade, while the hard white has a medium cut. The soft white cuts fast but the tool needs finishing on a finer stone.

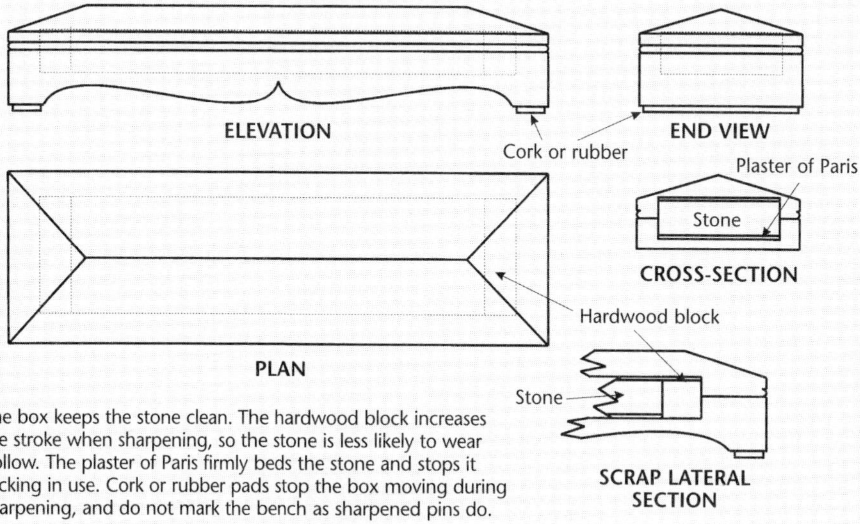

The box keeps the stone clean. The hardwood block increases the stroke when sharpening, so the stone is less likely to wear hollow. The plaster of Paris firmly beds the stone and stops it rocking in use. Cork or rubber pads stop the box moving during sharpening, and do not mark the bench as sharpened pins do.

Fig 5.2 Oil stone fitted into box.

Washita

This name is given to second-grade Arkansas stone. Very few new stones are sold under this name. The stone often comprises soft and hard patches.

Tam-o'-shanter

A fine-grained, soft, slate-like stone. It wears fast, cuts very slowly, and was never very popular.

Welsh slate

Over the years a number of companies have offered a particular type of slate as a sharpening stone, price being the main attraction. As fine finishing stones they work well, though slowly. However, the cut is very low. They work best when used with water.

Charnley Forest, also known as Whittle Hill stone

This is a greenish-grey-coloured stone of slate-like appearance. It is fine grained and makes a very good finishing stone. I have seen very few examples of this stone, though it was once very popular. It wears fairly rapidly, so I suppose that most old stones have just been worn out.

Water of Ayr, also known as Scotch stone and Snake stone

This stone is too soft for our purpose. Lithographic printers use it for correcting printing plates. In the past it has been offered in bench-stone sizes for woodworkers, but was never popular.

Green stone

Quarried on Snowdon, this is a fine-grained type of slate and as a finishing stone it works exceptionally well. This stone was once prized for sharpening surgical instruments. Small pieces that have been used for this purpose occasionally appear on the secondhand market.

Belgium

A dove-grey, fine-grained stone. This is a favourite with violin makers for sharpening their knives. It is available in fairly large sizes. A very useful bench stone, it cuts best when used with water.

Turkey

Although no longer available new it was once very popular. It is often obtainable secondhand, and is well worth acquiring. A clean stone has a dirty yellow appearance. The stone works best when used with thin oil.

Japanese

In Japan there are a number of quarries from which stone suitable for sharpening is dug. Not only does stone from each quarry differ, the stone from different strata in the same quarry has different characteristics. The stone is therefore named by the quarry and the strata from which it comes. Some of these stones are very expensive. I only have experience of two stones, but both were totally different from any other stone that I have used. The Toshi from Asweedo Quarry near Kyoto has an attractive mottled pink and cream surface. It cuts fast but the grains are fine. The other stone is from Honyama Quarry: this is light grey in colour with a deposit from an adjacent strata on the underside. I am told these stones consist of particles of quartz and sericite.

Man-made Stones

Many different materials have been used to make sharpening stones. Pulverized natural stone has been rebonded into blocks, though the manufactured abrasives previously described are mainly used. Man-made stones are so consistent, the grit size so uniform, and the price so reasonable that they are to be preferred to most natural stones.

The stones most stocked by retailers are manufactured by Norton. There are two different varieties of abrasive used: silicon carbide marketed as Crystolon, and aluminium oxide marketed as India. The Crystolon stones are cheaper and inferior to the India. Stones are graded as fine, medium and coarse. They are also made double-sided, with different grades on each side. For most purposes the coarse is too rough.

Japanese water stones

Japanese water stones have gained favour with Western woodworkers in recent years. These stones have a totally different character to those we have been accustomed to. They require a slightly different technique in use (see below), but this is soon acquired. The Japanese stones are graded by grit size, the coarsest being 100 mesh and the finest 8,000 mesh. These stones are, in my opinion, indispensable.

Diamond-plated surfaces

Diamond-plated surfaces have recently become available, and several designs are made by different manufacturers. Some of the cheaper diamond surfaces do not last long. Others are plated on to brass shim and glued to a base, but after a few months of use the shim parts company with the base. I have tried out most of the different varieties available and would recommend that made by DMT (Diamond Machining Technology). Their product is made in four colour-coded grades: green 1,200 mesh, red 600 mesh, blue 325 mesh and black 60 mesh. They are all obtainable in a variety of sizes suitable for different workshop applications. The plates are used lubricated with water. Diamonds are fast cutting and remain very flat, even after long use. I find even the 1,200 mesh too coarse for putting the final polish on the tool, but they are otherwise ideal sharpening tools.

Ceramic stones

Ceramic stones are the latest item to be added to the woodworker's sharpening arsenal. They are made by bonding together alumina particles (synthetic sapphires) in ceramic. The stones are fired at temperatures exceeding 3,000°F (1650°C). The ceramic stones are capable of cutting all known metals, and are used dry. They are made in a variety of grades. At the time of writing there are three grades available in the UK: medium, fine and ultra-fine. The ultra-fine grade is capable of polishing steel. The bench stones are 8in (203mm) long, 2in (51mm) wide and half an inch (13mm) thick. There are also a variety of shaped stone files. The ceramic stones are extremely hard, and wear is probably infinitesimal, but the stones have not long been available so it is impossible to be sure. As the stones are used dry, metal particles build up on the surface. The manufacturers say that the stone should be cleaned from time to time with a household cleaner and a soft abrasive pad (Scotch-Brite). I have used these stones in an experimental way for several months. They work best for me when used with water as a lubricant, not dry as instructed by the manufacturers. In this way they stay clean and the tool stays cool during sharpening. The small slip stones seem very fragile, but mine are still in one piece after normal use.

Honing Liquids

If steel is rubbed on a dry stone, metal will be removed, but the surface of the stone soon becomes clogged with metal particles. The clogged stone ceases to cut, and its surface becomes glazed, so a liquid is used to float away the metal particles as they are abraded from the steel. This liquid is sometimes incorrectly referred to as a lubricant. A lubricant is used to reduce friction, but this is not the purpose of the liquid in this case, although it does help to keep the steel cool. Its pupose is to remain on the surface of the stone in order to float the metal particles away from the stone's suface, and its consistency must therefore be sufficient to achieve this. Other than this criteria, any liquid that is freely available has at some time been used for honing. Oil sold as honing oil is expensive, and no better than machine or engine oil thinned with paraffin. Engine oil on its own is too thick, while paraffin on its own will clear the pores of the stone but runs off the surface. A little experimentation may be necessary to arrive at the correct proportions.

Soft stones such as slate and Belgium work better when used with water. When sharpening with water, wipe the tool with an oily rag when you have finished honing, as steel that has been sharpened using water has a tendency to rust unless it is oiled. Water kept in the workshop soon turns into a smelly, mucky liquid. A few crystals of permanganate of potash in the water will prevent this. Whatever liquid is used, it has to be wiped from the sharpened tool. The liquid is full of metal particles and is a black, mucky substance. It is very easy to contaminate work with this, so keep sharpening and work in progress well apart.

Japanese water stones are treated quite differently, however, and these are dealt with in a separate section below.

Bench Stones

Many tools are honed by rubbing them on a large flat stone called a bench stone. The size of the stone is important as a small stone is

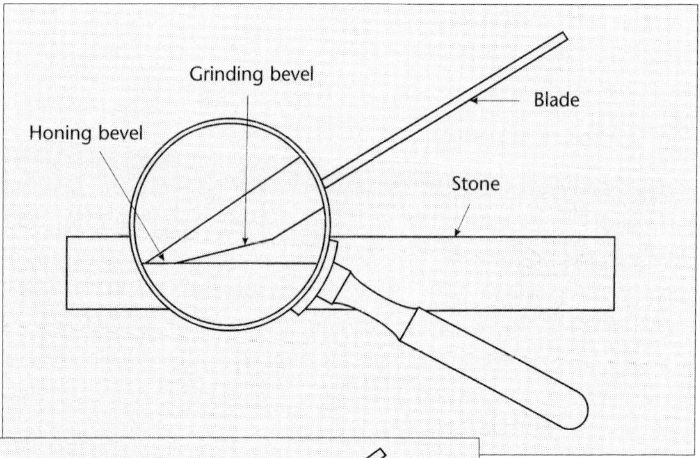

Fig 5.3 Correct method of honing a bevel flat on a stone.

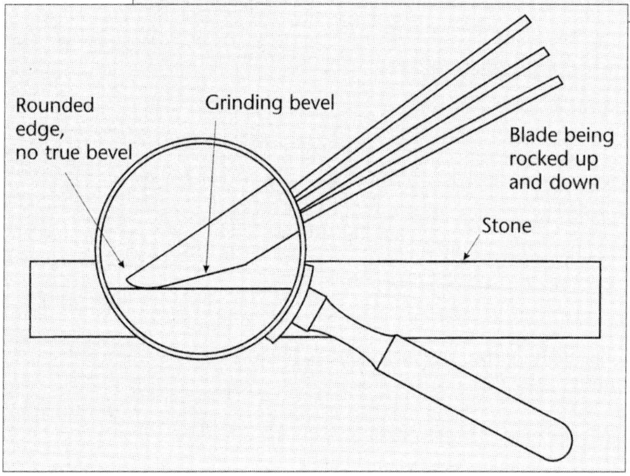

Fig 5.4 Rounded cutting edge caused by incorrect honing technique.

difficult to use with some tools. Most stones are 8in (203mm) long, 2in (51mm) wide and 1in (25mm) thick (though some stones are made considerably bigger than this), and I should say this is the minimum useful size for a bench stone. Honing is not just a matter of rubbing the tool back and forth on the stone, for so many things affect the ultimate cutting edge. We have established that the edge is formed by two flat planes meeting. Therefore the surface being honed must be kept flat (Fig 5.3). This is not as easy as it may seem. The slightest rocking up and down of the blade being honed will produce a rounded surface, not a flat plane (Fig 5.4). The height of the stone's surface, the way the tool is held and the flexibility of the

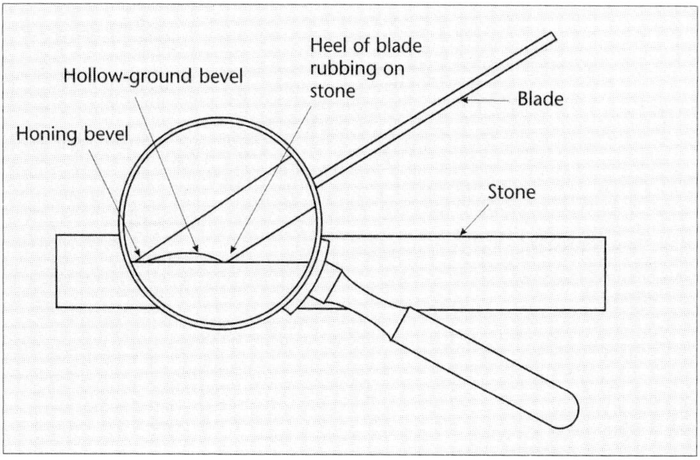

Fig 5.5 Hollow-ground method of honing.

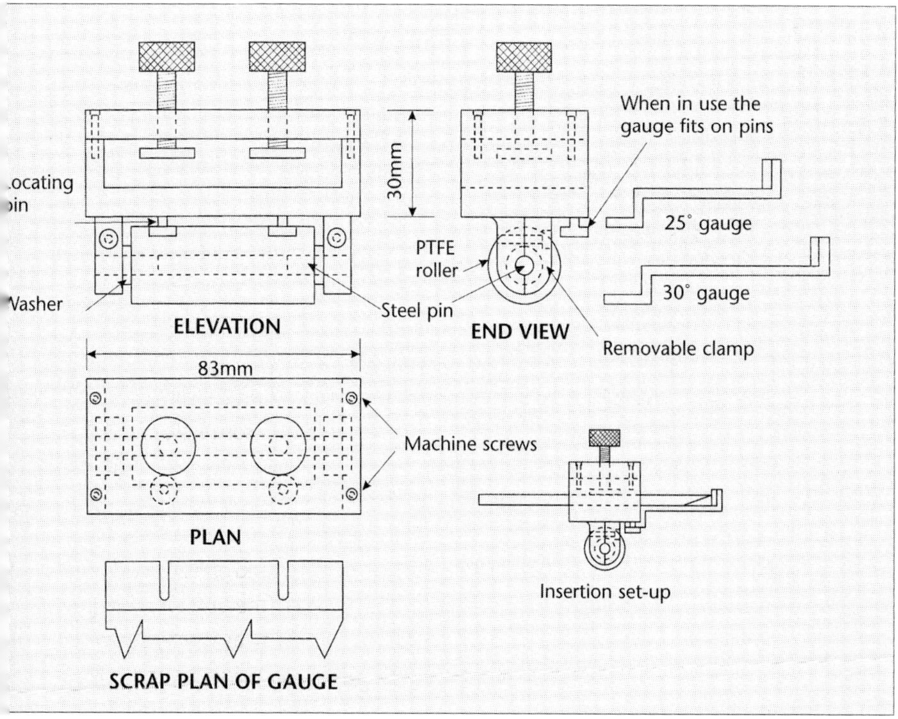

Fig 5.6 Workshop-made precision honing guide.

wrist and elbow all contribute to forming the correct flat bevel.

It is not easy to keep the narrow bevel flat on the stone, but there are two ways to help this process. The grinding bevel can be formed on a small-diameter wheel. This gives a hollow-ground bevel that can be used flat on the stone as shown in Fig 5.5. Alternatively, a device known as a honing guide can be used. Although many craftsmen look upon the honing guide with scorn, I believe that if a better cutting edge can be obtained using a device, then it should be used. I have therefore designed my own guide (Fig 5.6). Some devices have narrow metal rollers that wear the stone hollow; you should avoid these if possible, though it is often possible to modify them (Figs 5.7 and 5.8).

Slip Stones

Some tools have shaped cutting edges. These take two forms: there is the curved edge, as on the gouge, and the shaped edge,

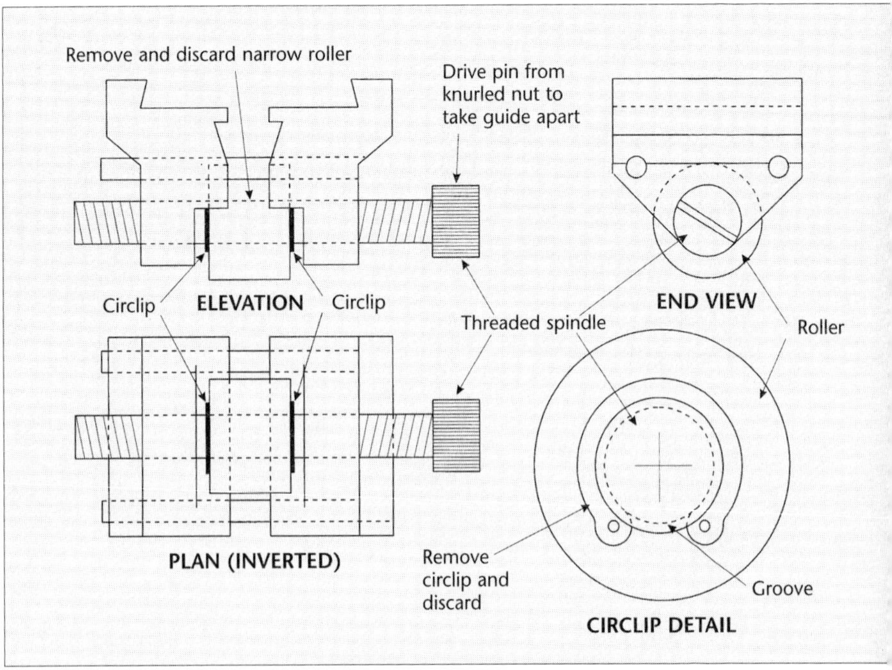

Fig 5.7 Eclipse 36 honing guide before modification.

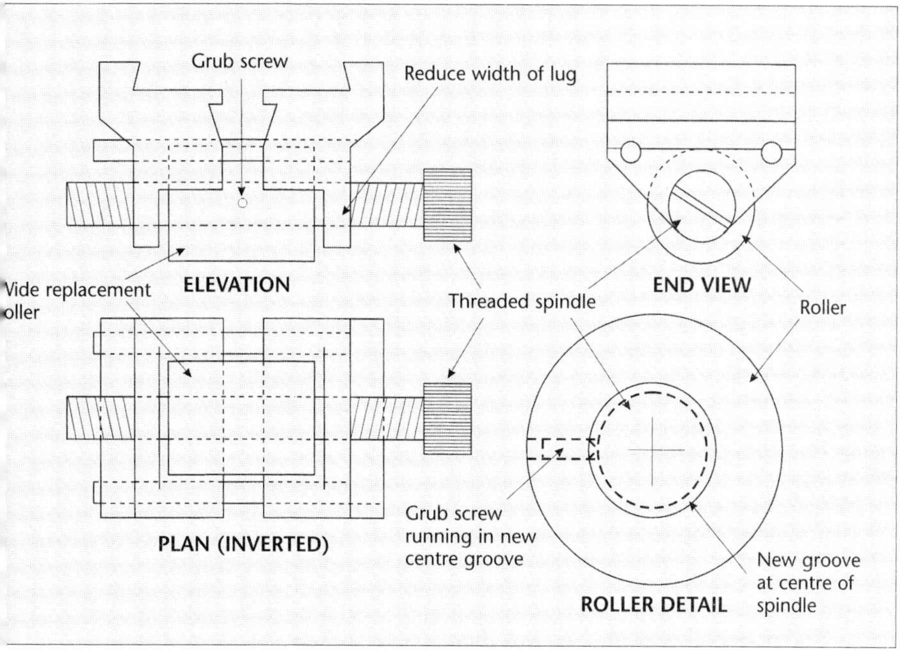

Fig 5.8 Eclipse 36 honing guide after modification.

as on a moulding plane or machine cutter. A shaped stone, called a slip stone, has to be used to hone these tools. In most cases the tool is held still and the stone rubbed on the honing bevel. It is even more difficult to keep the bevel flat than when using the

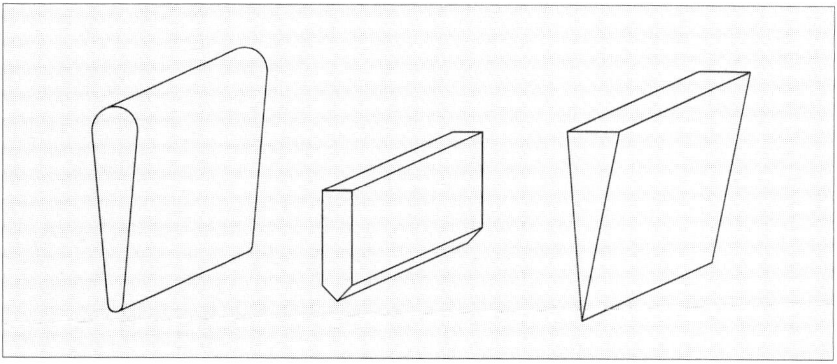

Fig 5.9 Different shapes of slip stones.

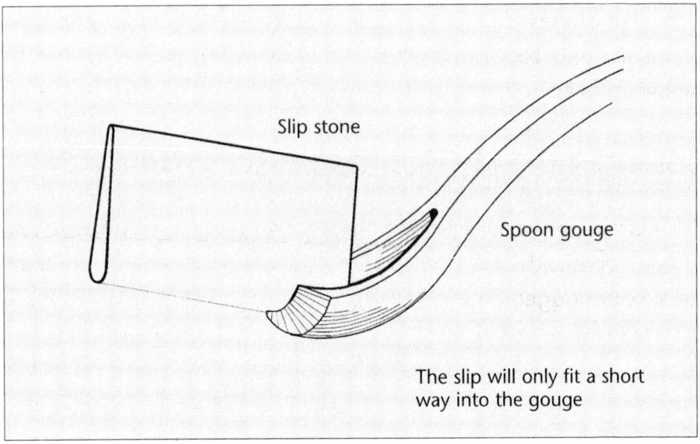

Fig 5.10 Sharpening a front-bend spoon gouge.

bench stone, and no honing device can be used. Slip stones are obtainable in several different shapes and sizes (Fig 5.9). For general use a slip 4in (102mm) long and 2in (51mm) deep is required. The thickness is dependent on the shape of the edges. Most slips have rounded edges, each edge having a different radius (Fig 5.10). Some slips have a very narrow edge, known as feather or knife edged. There is also an engineering tool called a stone file. This is a stick of sharpening stone 4in (102mm) long. They are square, round or triangular in section and made in a

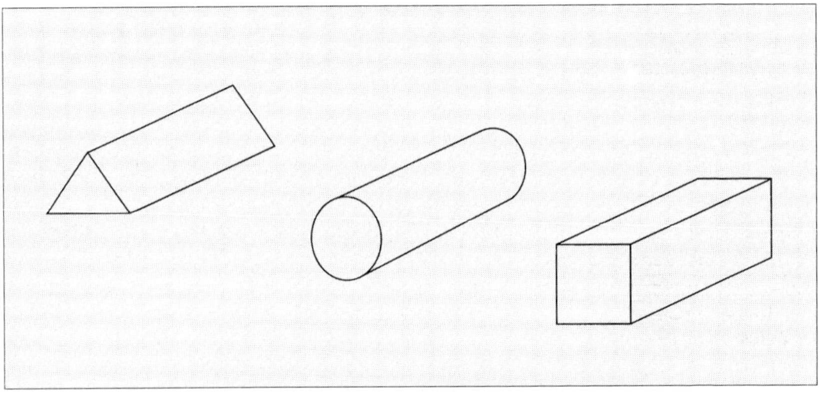

Fig 5.11 Stone files.

range of grades (Fig 5.11). These are very useful tools for honing woodworking tools. Slips and stone files need to be used with liquid, similar to bench stones.

Japanese Water Stones

The Japanese water stone is totally different from any traditional stone used in the Western world. They are porous and are used in a waterlogged state. To achieve this they are kept immersed in water when not in use. This is best achieved by making a special receptacle as shown in Fig 5.12. If only a single stone is used, the plastic container in which bulk ice cream is bought is

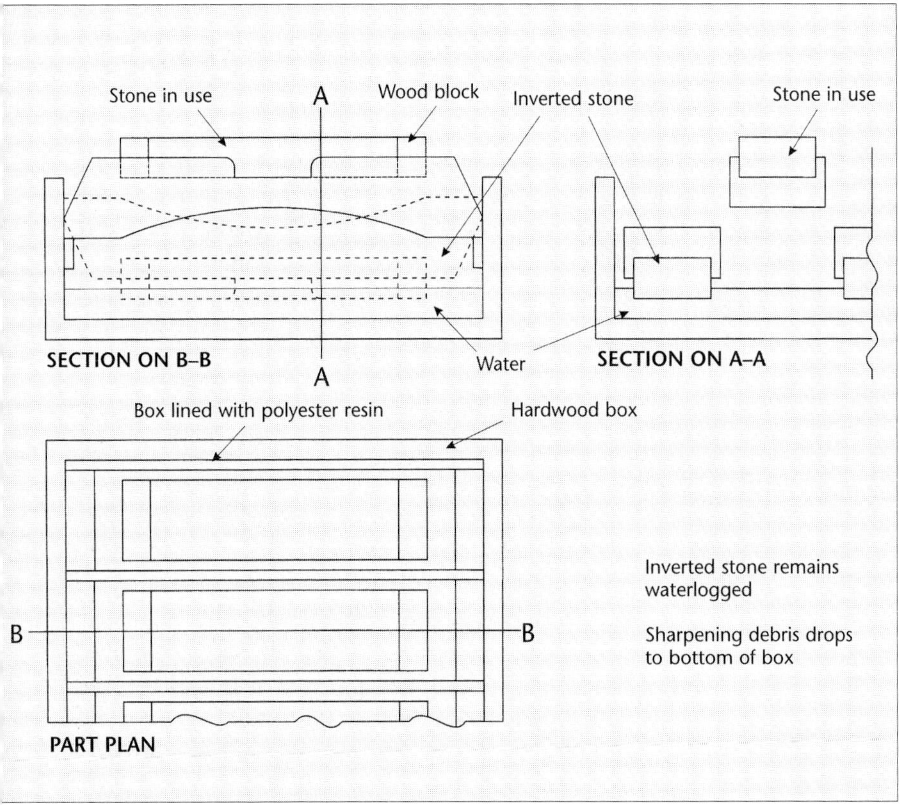

Fig 5.12 Japanese water stone box.

ideal to keep the stone submerged. Some Japanese stones are made in large sizes and depending on the tool being honed, these large stones can be a boon. Various shaped slip stones are also available. Because the stones are soft the surface breaks up all the time it is being used, and the grains breaking away form into a slurry on the surface of the stone. The grains of abrasive in this slurry continue to break down, so the texture of the slurry becomes finer and finer as the honing progresses. The slurry is an important feature of these stones, and you must resist the temptation to wash it off. The slurry is so important that a small stone, kept specially for the purpose, is rubbed over the surface to form a slurry before honing. This small stone is called a *nagura*. As the stones are soft they frequently need flattening, which is easily achieved by rubbing the faces of the stones against one another. However, I have found the best tool for this purpose is a diamond plate: the black (coarse grade) plate made by DMT is ideal.

Diamond Sharpening Surfaces

The manufacturers of diamond sharpening surfaces recommend that water is used when honing on them. This keeps the surface free of metal particles, but it runs off quickly and needs frequent replenishment. Diamond surfaces are made in a variety of shapes and sizes, and what has been said above about bench stones applies here. The shaped surfaces look similar to metal files. Brass shim plated with diamond can be glued to shaped wooden blocks, and in this way a sharpening surface of any shape can be formed. Some diamond surfaces are made of perforated plate, the manufacturers stating that these perforations help keep the surface clear of metal particles. However, they are a nuisance when sharpening narrow tools. Some diamond bench stones are supplied in decent wooden boxes, but if the plate is used in the box the water runs off into the box, which warps because of the moisture. A recent introduction is a Japanese waterstone made from diamond particles, which works extremely well as a medium-grade stone. However, the price puts it in the luxury rather than the useful tool class.

CHAPTER 6

Strops and Stropping

What is a Strop?

A strop is a piece of leather dressed with a very fine abrasive compound, and for woodworking comes in many shapes and sizes. A number of strops are needed to suit different tools. The craftsman makes his own strops, which are simple devices of leather glued to wood. The most common is a flat piece of leather about 10in (254mm) long and 2in (51mm) wide glued to a board (Fig 6.1). Sometimes the board has leather glued on both sides, each side being dressed with a different grade of compound. This compound, sold as strop dressing, comprises two different-coloured sticks resembling square-sectioned wax crayon packed in a small box. The black stick is made from a finer abrasive than the red. The dressing is conservatively scribbled on to the surface of the leather. The strops once dressed have a greasy surface that is inclined to pick up grit and debris from the surface of the bench, and this is the last thing on which we want to rub a cutting edge. The strop must be kept clean, and the best way of achieving this is to have a box-like sheath in which to store it. Smaller shaped strops need a proper box in which to live. Leather can be glued to the flat top of the lid of your oil stone box, so that you can easily strop the tool when you finish honing it, but I am not in favour of this as the leather becomes contaminated and does more damage than good.

Some tool shops sell a four-sided strop originally made for the hairdressing trade. Three sides are covered with leather, and the fourth has a fine honing stone fixed to it. In use, two sides are dressed with different compounds. The third leather face is left undressed, and is used as the final polishing surface. This is a useful tool for woodworkers. I am told that the best leather for making strops is horse hide but, not always being able to buy this, I have used the leather from which shoe repairers make soles and found it satisfactory. The smooth dressed side of the leather is used to strop. Contact adhesive is fine for sticking leather to wood.

Stropping the inside of small gouges such as those used for carving is usually done in one of two ways. The edge of a thick piece of leather is dressed and pulled down the cannel of the tool. Alternatively, a strip of leather resembling a bootlace is used. Larger gouges can be stropped by bending a piece of leather to fit inside their radius (Fig 6.2). A better method is to shape a piece of wood like a slip stone and glue leather round its surface (Fig 6.3). There is also a tool that

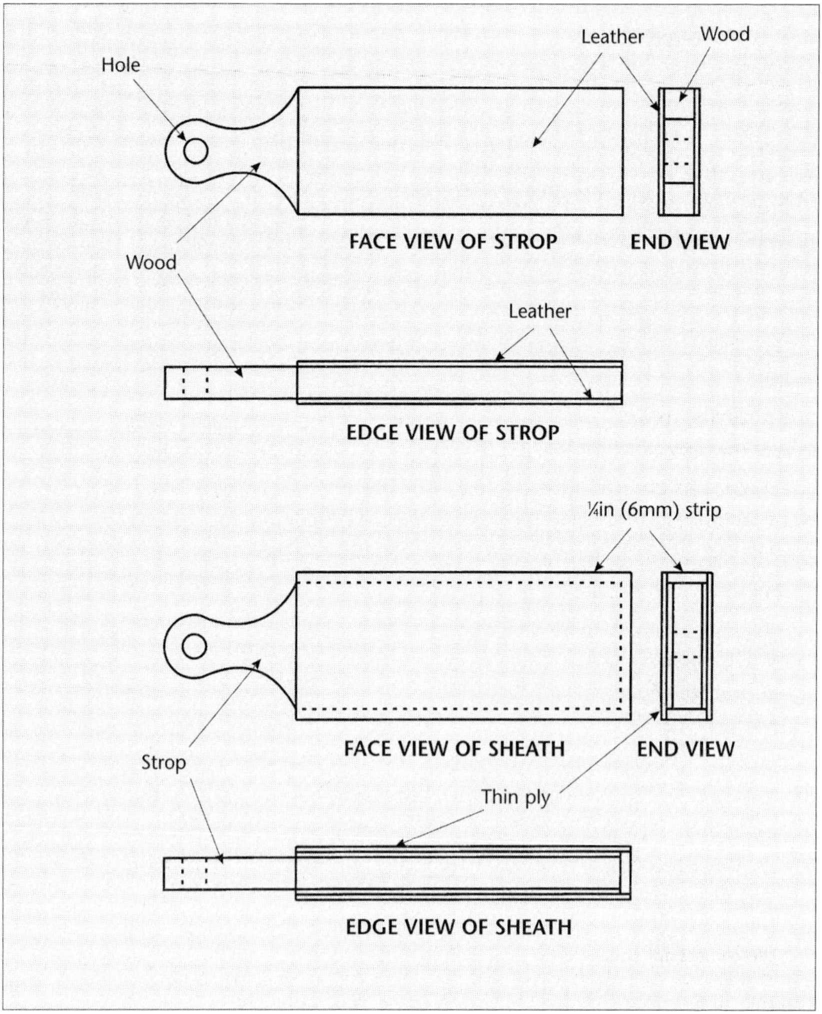

Fig 6.1 Strop and sheath.

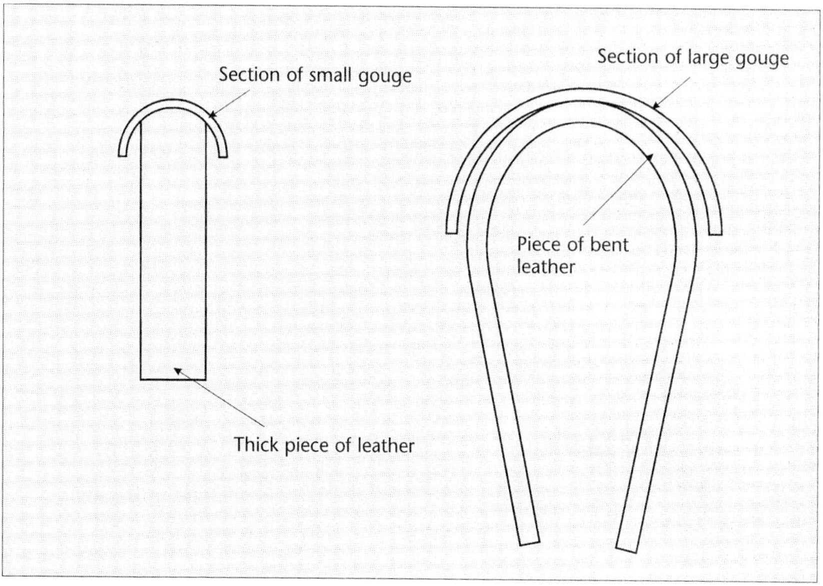

Fig 6.2 Stropping gouges with leather.

some carvers make (Fig 6.4); I have three of these in different sizes, which are sufficient to cover all the sizes of carving gouges that I use.

New strops do not work very well, as it takes time for the dressing to penetrate into the fibres of the leather. After a few weeks of use the surface of the strop takes on a smooth, almost shiny, appearance, and it then works well.

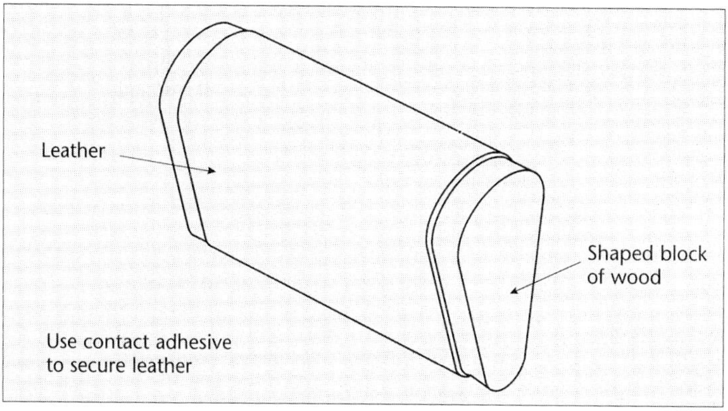

Fig 6.3 Stropping slip.

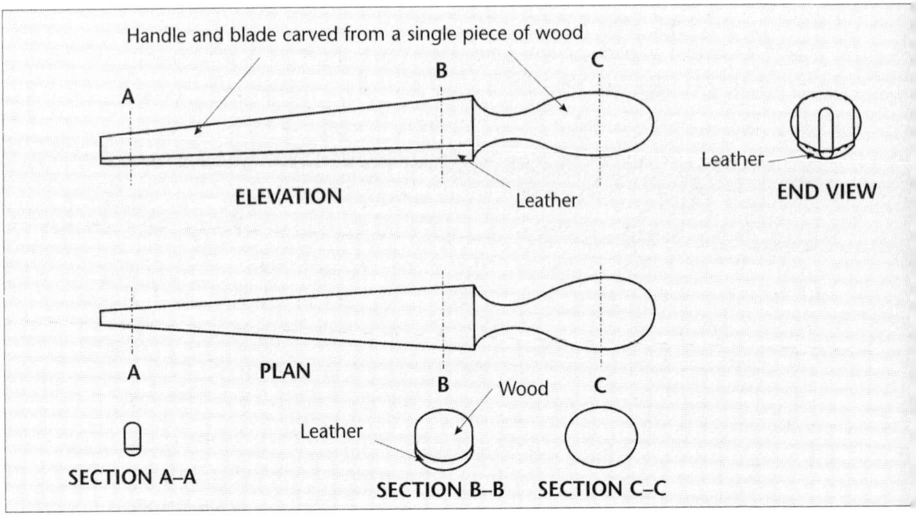

Fig 6.4 Shaped strop for gouges.

Why Strop?

I explained earlier that the sharpening process consisted of abrading metal away by using successively finer and finer abrasives. Stropping is the last and finest-grade process in the chain. For many woodworking processes stropping is not necessary. Where it comes into its own is when we are using tools to take delicate cuts and need a very sharp edge, which must be kept *very* sharp. The strop can be kept on the bench close to hand, and used every few minutes to restore the edge to its peak condition. In this way the time when the tool has to be honed is delayed, and the overall time spent in sharpening is reduced, as time spent in sharpening is non-productive.

Using the Strop

The flat strop is easier to use than those made to fit into gouges and other shaped tools. Because of the soft surface of the strop the tool can only be drawn backwards along its surface – it must not be pushed or it will dig in and damage the strop. When using a strop for the first time it is easiest if a flat tool such as a chisel or plane iron is stropped. Place the tool at the end of the strop with the honing bevel in contact with the surface. The tool should be at the same angle as it was when honed. Raise the angle about one degree and drag the tool along the strop (Fig 6.5). Lift the tool, return it to the end of the strop and repeat. Four or five strokes on each side of the strop should be sufficient. The tool is turned over and the flat face drawn along the strop in a similar fashion.

To strop a gouge is more difficult than dealing with a flat tool. Out-cannel tools are easier than in-cannel. The bevel of the out cannel can be placed on the flat hone, very much as described above for flat tools, the only difference being that a rolling action is applied as the tool is drawn along so that the whole of the cutting edge is treated. If small gouges are used a lot, you should have a separate strop for them. A groove is worn along the strop and, while this does not perfectly fit the sweep of all gouges, it works better than a flat surface.

In-cannel gouges are best held still and the strop rubbed on their inside bevel. It is important not to round off the bevel, so try to keep the strop at a constant angle to the edge. If you want both an inside and an outside bevel on carving gouges, the tool has to be treated as both in and out cannel.

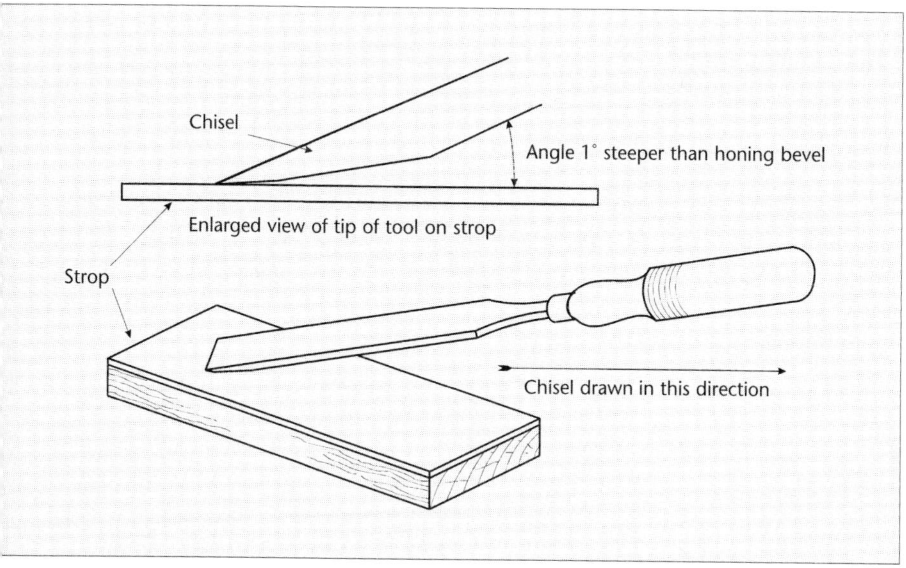

Fig 6.5 Stropping a chisel.

CHAPTER 7

Sharpening by Machine

Why Sharpen by Machine?

Time spent sharpening tools is essentially non-productive, therefore any mechanised aid to the process is welcome, providing satisfactory results are achieved. The machines discussed in this chapter are those designed to hone an edge (as opposed to grinding machines).

Fabric Buffing Wheels

Buffing is adopted by many woodcarvers. It is possible to make a machine for yourself using an electric motor and mounting buffing mops on its spindle, and many proprietary machines consist of only this. The wheels are sold in different sizes ranging from 3in (76mm) to 10in (254mm) in diameter, and the mops (buffing wheels) are made from several different materials. Sisal mops are made from a

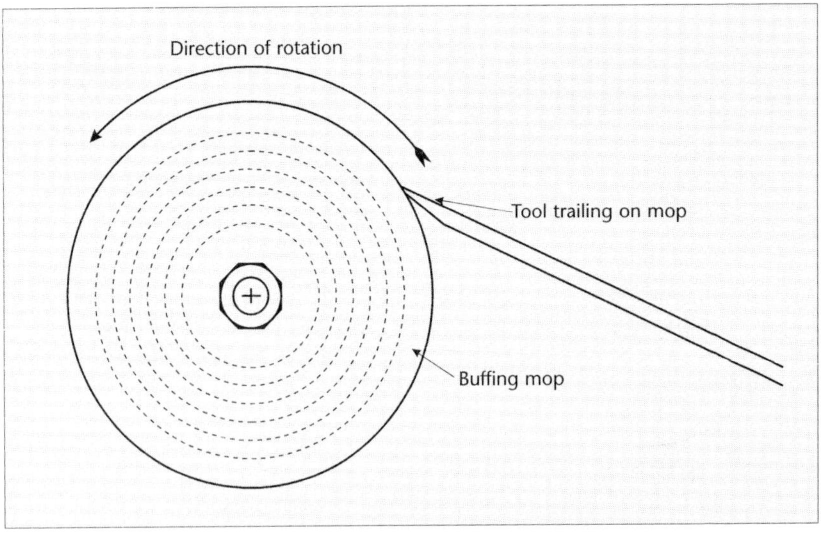

Fig 7.1 Sharpening on a buffing mop.

woven natural fibre covered with cotton and spiral-sewn. Sisal is a fast cutting medium and is used with a coarse dressing. Spiral-sewn cotton mops are made from specially selected cotton material with a large leather washer in the centre of both sides. These are finer and used less aggressively than the sisal mops. Canton flannel is used to make extra-soft mops for use with very fine abrasives. Felt wheels are harder than any of these, and their edge can be shaped to fit inside gouges. There are several grades of felt depending on the fibres from which it is made. Machines made for buffing metal sometimes have the mops held on a buffing taper, which is a tapered threaded device (Fig 7.2) called a 'pig's tail'. A version of the buffing taper that fits into the chuck of an electric drill is freely available, and it is thus possible to use an electric drill as a mechanical sharpening device.

Fig 7.2 Pig's tail screwed into a buffing mop.

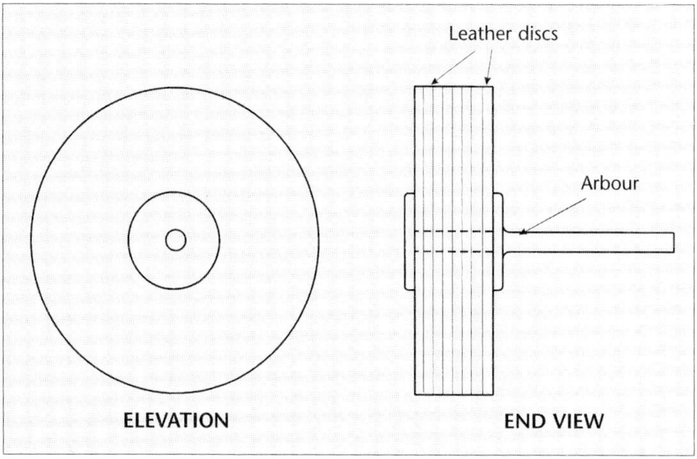

Fig 7.3 Leather sharpening wheel.

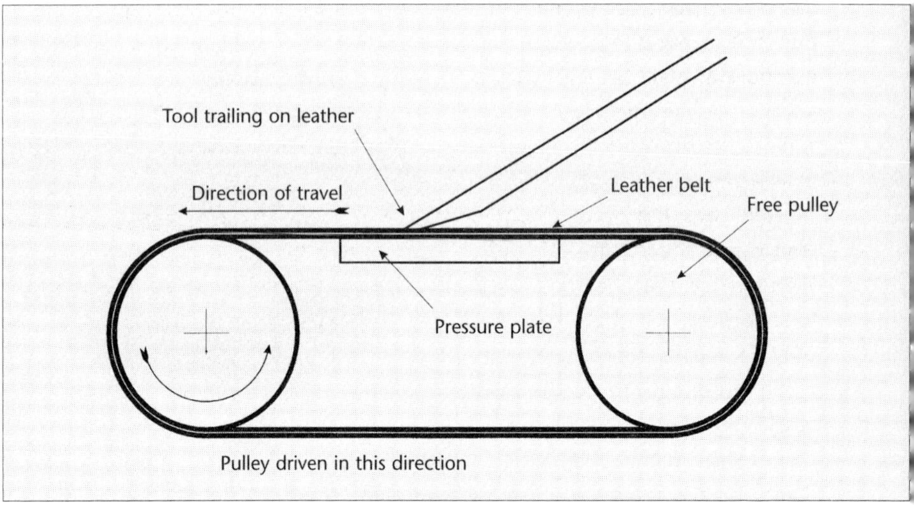

Fig 7.4 Sharpening on a leather belt.

Leather Wheels and Belts

Wheels made of leather are fitted on to a spindle very similar to the buffing wheels (Fig 7.3), and are made of several large discs of leather usually held together at their centre by rivets. A leather belt on a sharpening machine is usually 1in (25mm) wide, an endless loop of leather. It runs on two pulleys, one free and the other power driven. At the top of the loop where the sharpening takes place the leather runs over a fixed metal plate, which supports the leather when a tool is pushed against it. Tilgear market a leather wheel that can be fitted into the chuck of an electric drill; it comes complete with arbour and is ready for use. The Tormek grinder has a large wheel that has its circumference covered with leather. I have not found the various means of sharpening on power driven leather very successful.

Abrasive Compounds

There are numerous compounds marketed for use with buffing mops, but be careful when choosing. Most emery compounds are too aggressive. Tripoli compound works well, as does jeweller's rouge, and the dressing made from white rouge is the finest grade that I have been able to find. This works extremely well for putting that final, very sharp edge on carving tools. Some retailers sell compounds made especially for sharpening machines, though these seem to vary enormously. The compound's grade can be judged by rubbing a smear of it between thumb and finger. If it feels gritty it is too coarse.

After considerable use the surface of the buffing wheel may be clogged by compound and metal particles, but there is a tool called a 'Mop Rake' that is used to clean the wheel's surface. The rake has four rows of sharp teeth that are lightly pressed against the surface of the revolving mop.

Safety

Do not wear loose clothing or neck ties when sharpening by machine, as they can become entangled with the revolving parts of the machine. Roll up loose sleeves. Protect your eyes with safety glasses or goggles. Make sure that the tool being sharpened trails on the sharpening surface, that is to say, the sharpening surface moves away from the cutting edge. If this is not observed the tool digs into the sharpening surface and an accident can result.

Different Machines

It is difficult to compare machines without taking their price into consideration. If you only do woodcarving now and then as a pastime you probably will not want to invest a couple of hundred pounds in a sharpening machine, though it is not difficult to construct a sharpening machine by using a motor from a scrapped washing machine.

Below is a brief description of some of the machines I have used, though many more are available, and the type of machine that will suit you will depend upon your individual requirements.

The **Hegner** is the most expensive and probably the best-made machine that I have used. It has four felt wheels and a driven belt. The end of the spindle on which the wheels are mounted is fitted with a drill chuck. One of the felt wheels is narrow and has a rounded edge that fits inside most medium and large gouges. The tool rest is an adjustable round bar. The machine is supplied with an abrasive belt fitted. The only fault I can find with the machine is the noise from the belt mechanism.

The **Kurt Kotch** machine is the simplest of all that I have used, and for me it is the best. It comprises an electric motor with an extended spindle on which are mounted two felt wheels, one composed of coarse fibres and the other of fine fibres. The tool rest is made from a block of wood, which fulfils its purpose very well.

The **Tormek** sharpening machine is sold as a complete sharpening system. The machine consists of a wet abrasive wheel, which has a unique feature – the cutting characteristic of the wheel changes depending on which side of the dressing stone (supplied with the machine) is used. When the coarse side of the dressing stone is used the wheel works as a normal wet grinder. When the wheel is dressed with the smooth side it takes on the characteristics of a fine hone. On the other side of the machine is a metal and plastic wheel, which is covered by a 1in (25mm) wide strip of leather. A tube of compound is supplied for dressing this. Numerous attachments are obtainable as extras for jig grinding, a whole host of cutting tools ranging from scissors to planing machine blades.

The **Elu** machine is a high-speed bench grinder fitted with a belt attachment and, apart from the spark guard, is extremely well made. The belt attachment can be fitted with an abrasive or leather belt. The leather belt works very well on flat tools such as chisels.

The **Warco** is a low-priced example of a type of machine that uses a different principle from those above. The high-speed grinding part is as found on many machines, but the sharpening part is a circular Japanese water stone. This revolves at low speed and is kept wet by a drip feed from the water hopper fitted above the wheel. This is an ideal set-up for sharpening chisels and plane irons. Some care is required in using the stone as it is soft and easily damaged, but this is so with nearly all Japanese water stones.

The **Record Scan** machine is a simple wet grinder fitted with a rubber wheel that is impregnated with abrasive. The rubber wheel is driven by friction from the wet grinding wheel. I find the grinder an ideal machine but the sharpening side leaves much to be desired.

CHAPTER 8

Planes

The plane is probably the most sophisticated tool the woodworker uses. It was certainly the last of the major tools to be invented. Sharpening and setting the plane for use requires that its operation is fully understood. The finely set plate iron removes the top layer of fibres in the form of a shaving. The wedge shape of the cutting edge forces the fibres apart and they split in front of the iron's edge. As the cut shaving runs up the face of the iron it forms a lever which further accentuates the splitting action. If this splitting action is allowed to form uncontrolled the planed surface will be torn, particularly where the fibres are at an inclined angle to the surface of the wood. There are three ways this splitting tendency can be controlled (Fig 8.1). A second iron, called a back iron, can be fixed to the cutting iron. The back iron is shaped so that it breaks up the shaving and reduces the length of the lever, and its edge can be set

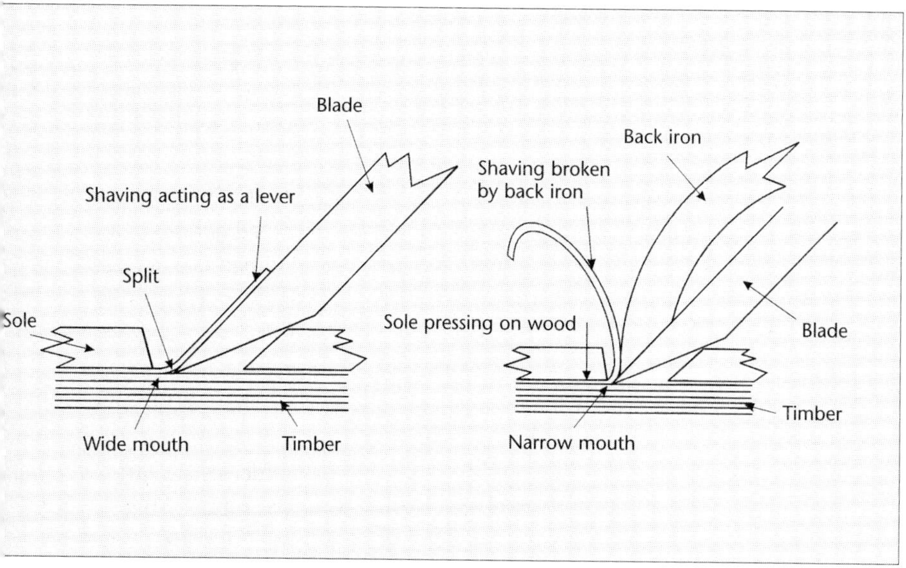

Fig 8.1 Cutting a controlled shaving.

very close to the cutting edge. The size of the plane's mouth also has an effect on preventing splitting. Lastly, the sole of the plane immediately in front of the mouth presses down on the surface of the wood, preventing the fibres from parting. Not all planes have a back iron. Low-angled planes intended for use on end grain have a single iron. Most single-ironed planes have the blade inserted with the bevel uppermost.

The Pitch

The angle between the plane's iron and sole is called the 'pitch of the iron'. The lower the angle the less is the energy required to push the plane. However, the tendency for the grain to split in front of the cut

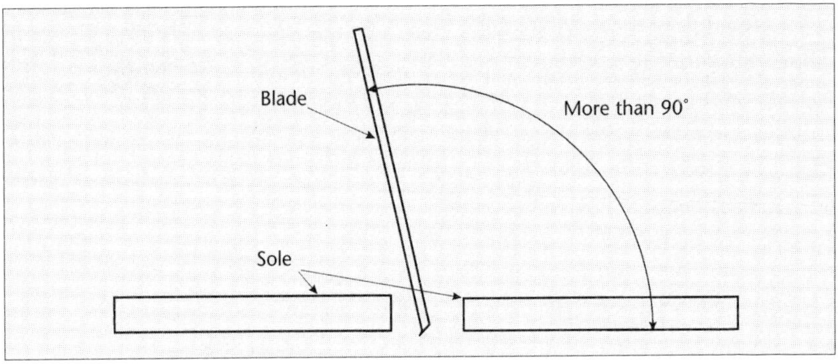

Fig 8.2 Scraper plane with negative pitch.

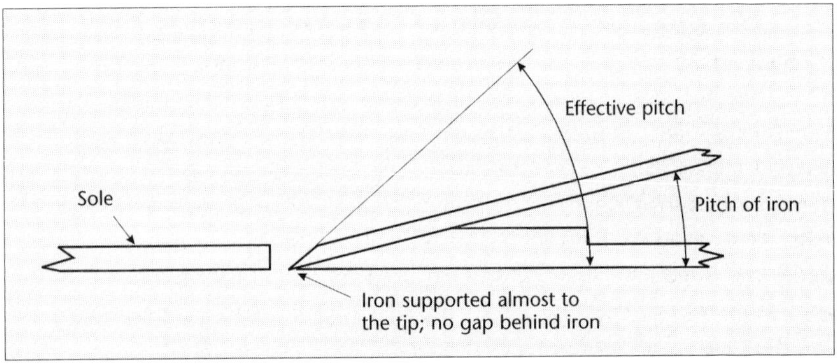

Fig 8.3 Effective pitch of a single iron with bevel uppermost.

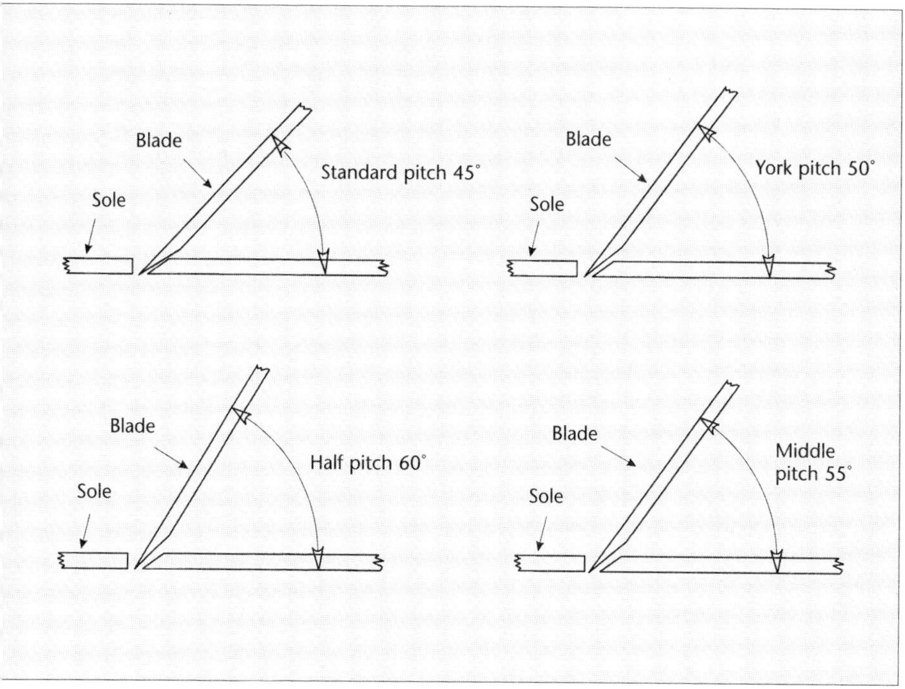

Fig 8.4 Pitch of plane irons.

is increased as the pitch is lowered. As the pitch of the iron is increased the cutting action of the blade becomes more of a scraping action. In fact, some scraper planes have a negative pitch angle, that is to say, the blade is pitched in excess of 90° (Fig 8.2). With single-ironed planes with the bevel uppermost, the sharpening angle of the blade becomes part of the effective pitch (Fig 8.3). The main advantage of having a blade inserted with the bevel uppermost is the way the back of the iron beds on to the body of the plane, which makes for a more precise cutting action and there is no gap behind the iron to catch on the point of mitres.

Planes with shaped irons, such as moulding planes, do not have back irons, because they would be difficult to fit. The irons in these planes are fitted with the bevel down, and to prevent the grain from being torn when using these tools the iron is pitched steeper than standard. Standard pitch (sometimes referred to as common pitch) is 45°, which is fine for general work (Fig 8.4). A steeper

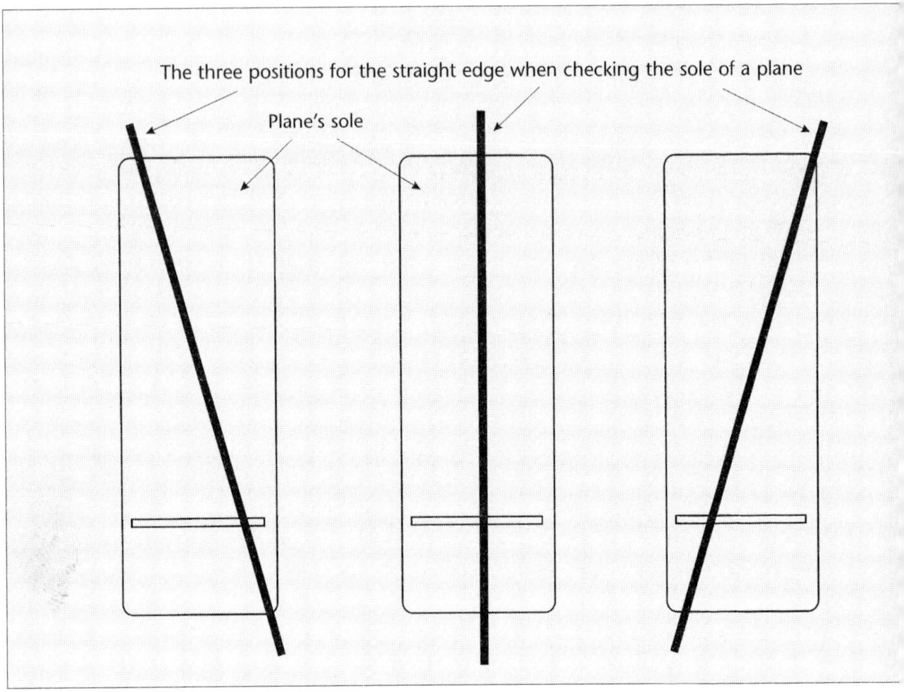

Fig 8.5 Checking a plane's sole for truth.

pitch is helpful when planing difficult-grained wood. Some cabinet-makers have a smoother with an iron pitched at 50°, which is known as a York pitch, and some use smoothers with irons pitched at 55° (middle pitch). Occasionally moulding planes have irons as steep as 60° (half pitch).

The Sole

If the plane is to work properly when planing flat wood its sole must also be flat. However, many metal planes are made from cast steel, which has internal stresses and tends to warp particularly in the first few years of its life. Check the sole of the plane using a good metal straight edge (Fig 8.5). If the sole is out of true it must be flattened.

Flattening can be done in several ways. The easiest is to have it surface ground by an engineer, but this is expensive and will probably cost more than the plane is worth. The sole can be rubbed flat on a

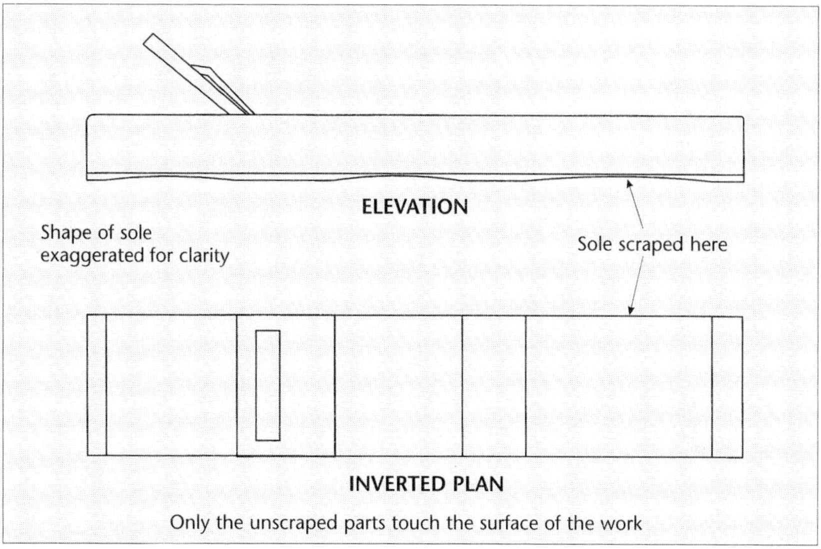

Fig 8.6 Japanese plane, showing the sole scraped to reduce friction.

piece of float glass using Carborundum powder or paste, and if it is badly out of true metal can be removed by using an engineer's scraper. Wooden-bodied planes are easily trued by planing them. An exception to flat-soled planes is the Japanese plane, the sole of which is prepared with a small scraper plane called a *dai-naoshi-kanna.* A wave pattern is formed on the sole, which reduces friction between the sole and the wood being planed (Fig 8.6).

When checking the sole of any plane for truth it is important that the iron is inserted and tightened, though it must be set shy of the face of the sole so as not to interfere with the straight edge. The tensioning of the blade in the plane body causes it to distort slightly, which needs to be taken into consideration when flattening or testing for truth.

The Iron's Shape

Jointing and rebating planes have straight cutting edges on their irons. Jack planes, however, have a curved cutting edge; the shaving is thicker in the centre than at its edges, which allows the plane to take thick shavings. Trying and fore planes have a straight cutting edge with just the square corners of the edge removed, while smoothing planes have the corners of the iron rounded off (Fig 8.7). The reason for these different shapes is to deal with the tasks for which the plane is used. An iron that is perfectly straight removes a shaving that is the same thickness throughout its entire width, so the surface of the wood being planed has a shallow groove where the shaving has been removed. There is a step in the surface the thickness of the shaving, so for most purposes the corners of the cutting edge are removed.

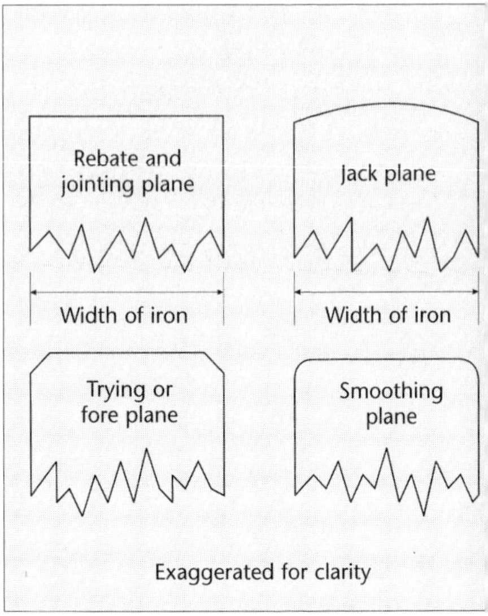

Fig 8.7 Shape of the cutting edge of plane irons.

Fitting the Back Iron

The back iron, sometimes called the 'chip breaker', needs special attention, particularly when new. As the shaving has to be deflected from the face of the blade and directed up over the back iron it is important that this path is made as smooth as possible. If there is the slightest gap between the back iron and the face of the blade the shaving will jam in it. The rest of the shaving being removed from the wood piles up, gagging the mouth of the plane which ceases to cut. The first task is to make sure that the face of the cutting iron is perfectly flat. Many new irons are badly ground by the manufacturer, and they have to be flattened by rubbing on a stone. A diamond plate is the best surface for this, as it is very flat. However, the iron's surface needs a final polish on a very fine stone to remove the small scratches left by the diamonds. When the face of the iron is in a satisfactory state, assemble the back iron on the blade, making sure the securing screw is tightened. Hold the assembled irons up to the light and try to sight between them. Any light showing means the fit is not good enough. The edge of the back iron that beds on to the face of the blade is rubbed on a flat hone to true it. Once the fit is correct, check the tip of the back iron where it meets the face of the blade. There must be no step here; if there is, file it away and then polish the surface with fine abrasive paper to remove the file marks. The back iron is made from unhardened steel and is easy to file.

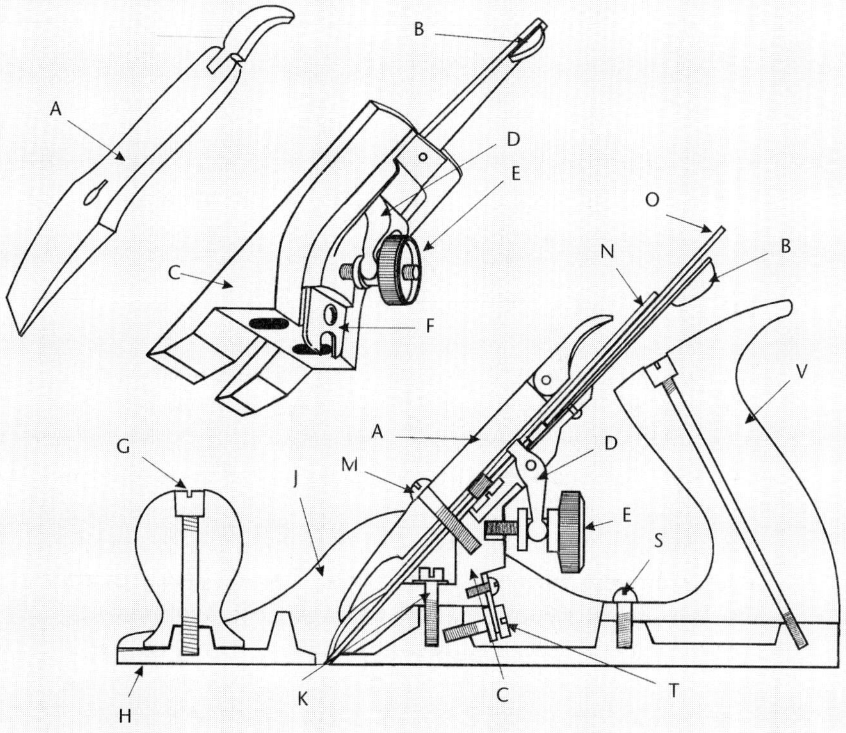

A Lever cap
B Lateral adjuster
C Frog
D Yoke adjusting lever
E Depth of cut adjuster
F Frog locating plate
G Knob bolt and nut
H Sole
J Plane body
K Frog screw
M Cap screw
N Back iron
O Iron (blade)
S Handle bolt
T Frog adjusting screw
V Handle

Fig 8.8 Bailey pattern plane.

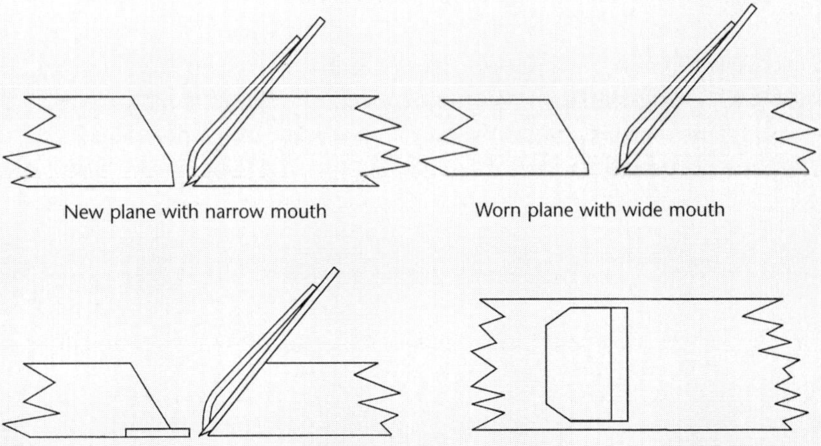

Fig 8.9 Remouthing a wooden plane.

The Mouth

The width of the mouth has an effect on the plane's performance, so it is important that the width can be set to suit the work for which the plane is used. The Bailey pattern plane has an adjustable frog (Fig 8.8). The frog can be moved in the body casting, thus moving the iron assembly nearer or further from the front of the mouth opening. Some block planes have inserts in their soles that are movable so as to alter the mouth's width, while some superior wooden planes made in Germany have adjustable hardwood inserts. Incidentally, wooden planes can always be remouthed when worn by inlaying a slip of hardwood in front of the mouth (Fig 8.9). The jack plane that is used for the rough preparation of timber takes a thick shaving, which needs a wide mouth through which to escape, whereas the polishing plane that takes a microscopically thin shaving to leave a finely finished surface requires the smallest mouth possible. British-pattern planes made for the top end of the trade are precision instruments, and are made with very small mouths commensurate with the work for which they are intended (Fig 8.10).

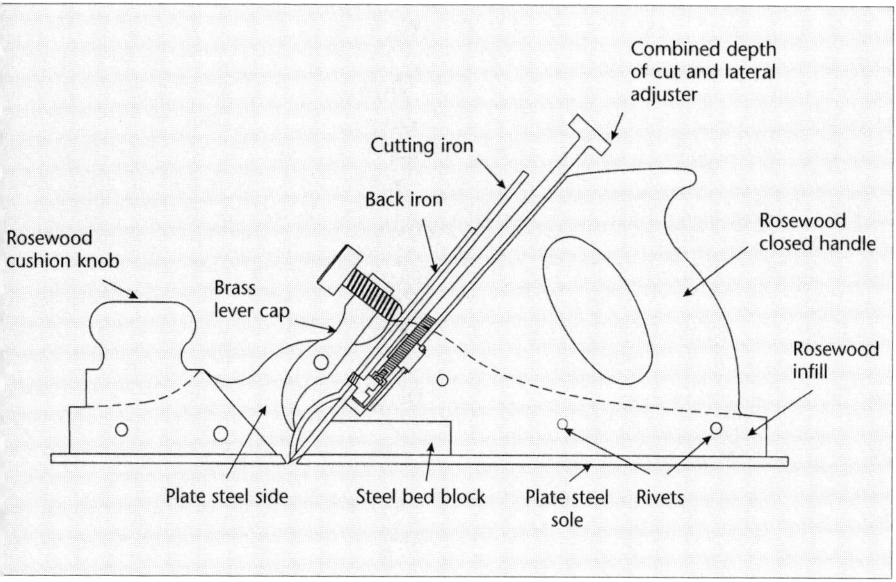

Fig 8.10 British-style plane.

New planes, both wooden and cast metal, often need some work carried out on their mouths. Any small roughness that might hinder the path of the shaving must be smoothed. The front of the mouth on some new metal planes is left unfettled and needs particular attention (Fig 8.11).

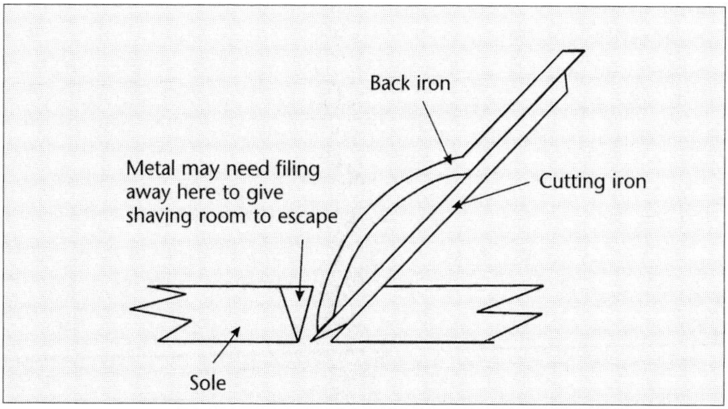

Fig 8.11 Ensure that nothing obstructs the shaving's escape path.

CHAPTER 9

Chisels

The term chisel is used here to describe only tools with a flat, straight cutting edge. Gouges and other shaped tools are discussed in Chapters 10 and 11. The cutting edge varies with the purpose for which the tool will be used. Some chisels are driven with a mallet to remove large pieces of wood, while others are used for paring thin shavings.

Carving Chisels

Carving chisels are made in widths ranging from 1/32in (1mm) to 1in (25mm). Very narrow tools need treating carefully when honing or the edge become misshapen. The corners of the cutting edge are a most important feature of all carving tools, the pointed corner on skew chisels needing particular attention. Many carvers sharpen their chisels with equal bevels on both sides, however the included angle of the bevels forming the edge varies according to the nature of the wood being worked – hardwood requires a stronger edge than softwood. Experiment with different angles, and you will soon be able to judge the type of edge required. Angles in the range 23° to 32° are the most useful (Fig 9.1).

Firmer Chisels

The most common woodworking chisel is the firmer, which is manufactured with both square and bevelled edges, in widths from 1/16in (2mm) to 2in (51mm). The square edge, being more robust than the bevelled edge, is used for heavier work.

Firmer chisels are used for such a wide range of tasks that sharpening will depend on the work the chisel will be asked to perform. Upholsterers use a firmer chisel for ripping out material held by cut tacks by driving it under the heads of the tacks, tearing them from the wood. A sharp edge is thus not needed, as it would only last a few seconds. The cabinet-maker cutting fine dovetails

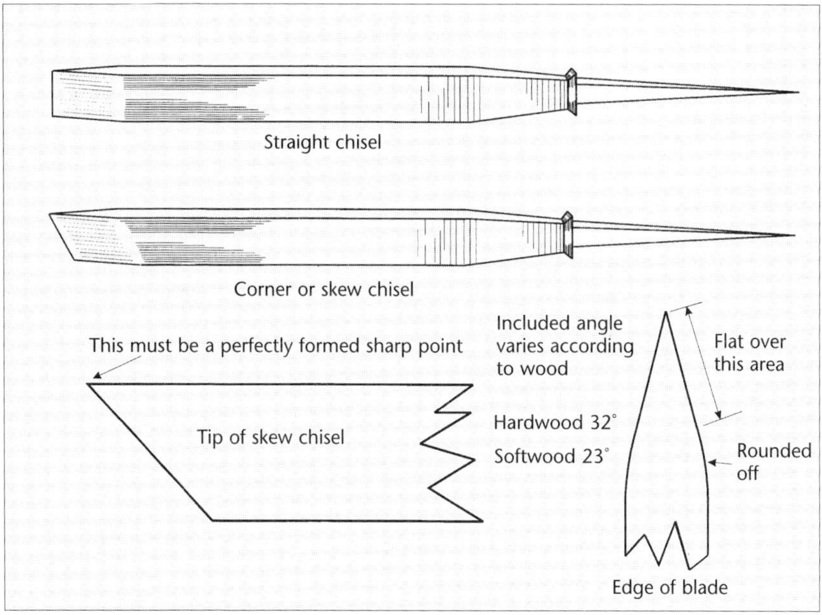

Fig 9.1 Carving chisels.

requires a bevelled-edge chisel with the bevel ground so that there is no square left on the edge of the tool. This chisel will fit right into the corner of the dovetail socket and needs to be very sharp. For a task like this a honing bevel around 25° is required. The site carpenter hanging doors will use a firmer chisel with a mallet to chop the butts into the door and frame. A honing bevel of 30° would be suitable.

Paring Chisels

The long blade of the paring chisel, when compared with that of a firmer chisel, gives the user better control over the cutting action of the tool. It should be used only for paring, and is never driven with a mallet. The edge has to be kept extremely sharp, and the tool works best if the grinding angle is kept low, around 20°, and the honing bevel no wider than 1/32in (1mm). The tool then not only enters the work with little effort, but the user is able to see and control the cutting edge. Narrow paring chisels from 1/8in

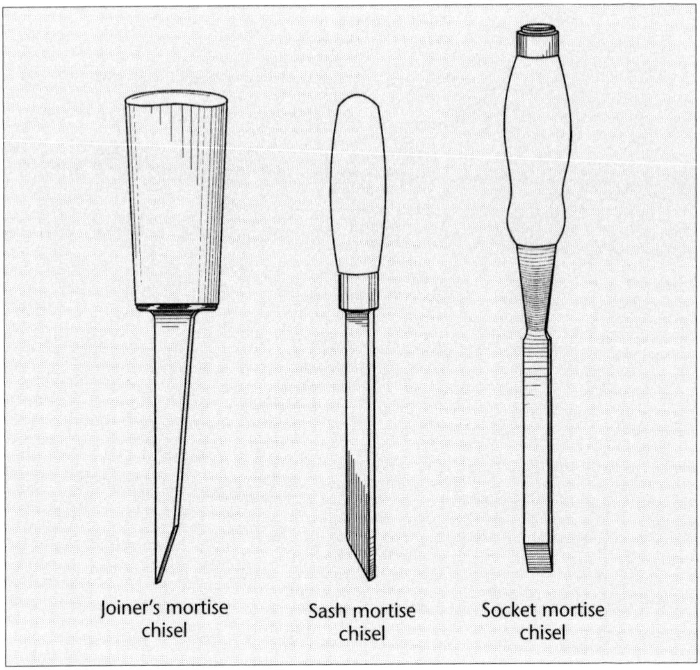

Fig 9.2 Mortise chisels.

(3mm) to ½in (12mm) need care when sharpening to ensure that the end is kept square.

Mortise Chisels

There are several designs of mortise chisel (Fig 9.2). The strongest is the joiner's mortise chisel and the lightest the sash mortise chisel. All are sharpened in a similar way. Because the process of chopping a mortise entails driving the chisel with a mallet, the tool's edge has to stand up to hard work. The honing bevel needs to be wide, at least ⅛in (3mm), and at 30° or steeper. The top of the grinding bevel, where it meets the back of the chisel, is rounded. This round bears on the side of the mortise when the chisel is used to lever chips from the mortise. A sharp corner would damage the mortise, but the round spreads the load (Fig 9.3). Clearing the bottoms of blind mortises is difficult without special tools. The swan neck chisel (not

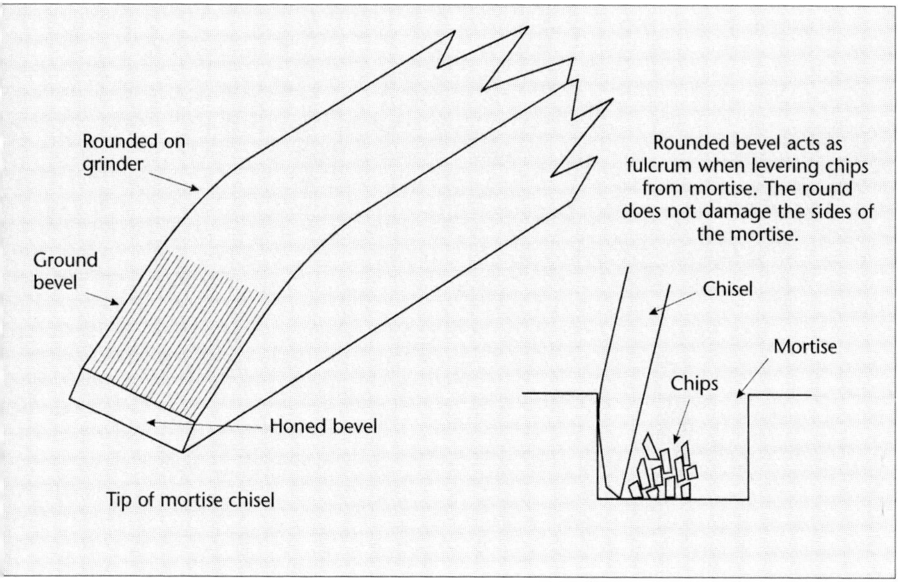

Fig 9.3 Sharpening a mortise chisel.

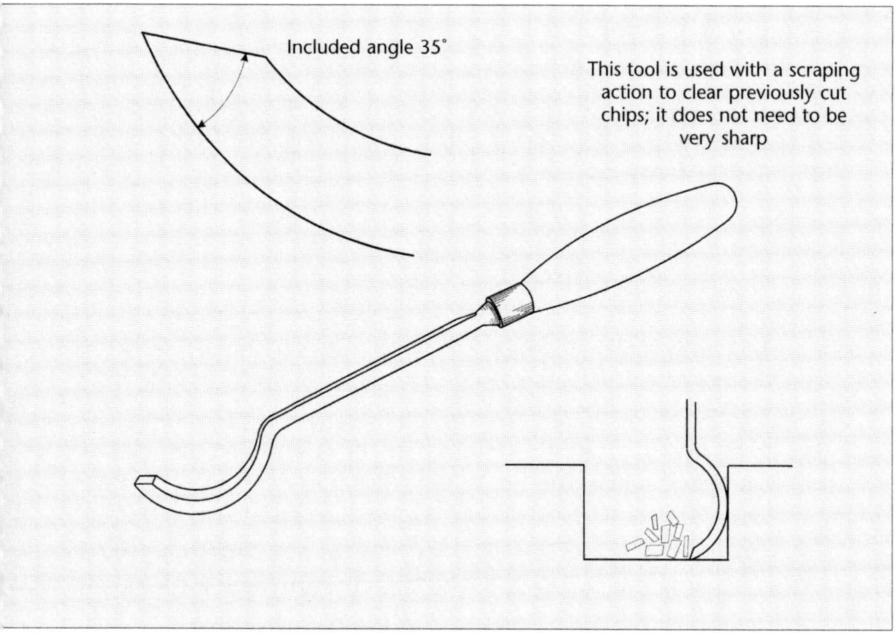

Fig 9.4 Swan neck mortise chisel.

to be confused with the swan neck mortise lock chisel) is designed for this purpose (Fig 9.4). Because of its shape this is a difficult tool to sharpen, as the bend in the blade makes it impossible to grind or hone in the normal way. The tool has to be turned at 90° to the length of the stone when honing. Grinding can only be accomplished on a wheel that is suitable for grinding on its side.

Turning Chisels

The amount of cutting done, and the time in which it is accomplished, means that turning chisels need frequent sharpening. The volume of work done over a short period not only blunts the tool but generates heat which also spoils the cutting edge. Turning chisels are thus made thicker than other chisels to get this heat away from the edge. The included angle of the cutting edge is 30° or more. The bevels forming the edge are flat – there is no second honing bevel, because the tool is controlled by the bevel rubbing on the work. Some turners use the chisel straight from the grindstone, but this is not recommended. A properly ground and honed chisel should leave the surface of the workpiece smooth and almost shiny.

Both square-ended and skew chisels are sharpened in a similar way. The point on the skew is important, and needs particular attention to make sure it has a perfectly sharp point. Because of their length, turning chisels are more difficult to hone than other woodworking chisels. Keeping the bevel flat on the stone requires practice.

Japanese Chisels

The best Japanese chisels are handmade by individual blacksmiths. The blade is made by wrapping a very hard piece of thin steel around the face of a soft steel block (Fig 9.5). Japanese chisels are not purchased in a ready-to-work condition. The first task to be undertaken when preparing a new chisel, therefore, is to flatten the face. This is done by rubbing it on a flat, soft steel plate about 8in (203mm) long, 2in (51mm) wide and ¼in (6mm) thick (called a *uraoshi* or *kanaban*) dressed with Carborundum powder. The face of the chisel has a hollow (*ura*) running down its length, though some chisels have several, depending on the maker. The hollows allow the

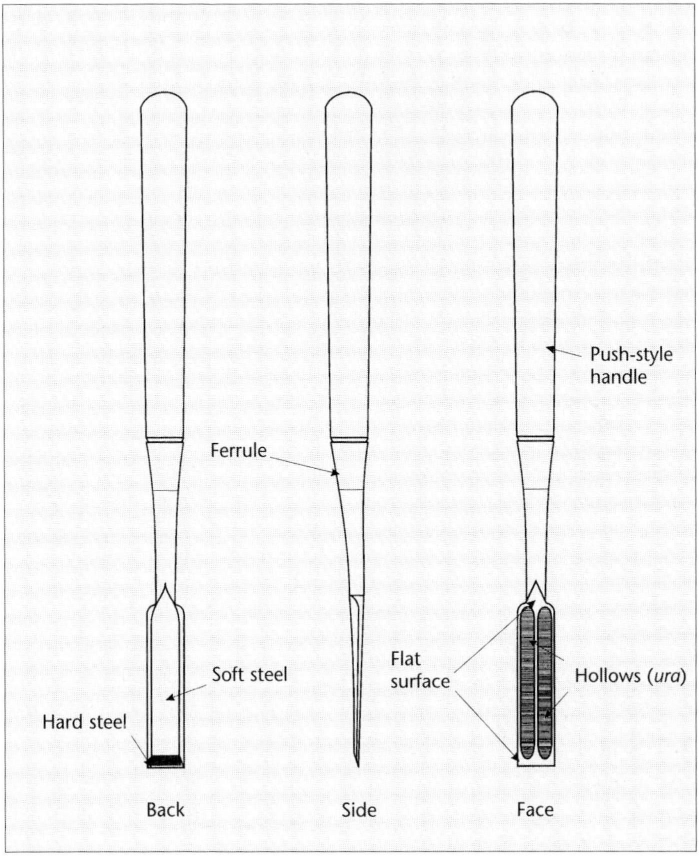

Fig 9.5 Japanese thin chisel (*Usu-nomi*).

face of the cutting edge to be quickly flattened. In use the narrow, flat strip between the hollow and the edge becomes too narrow. The face is rubbed on the *uraoshi* until the flat strip widens.

There are two types of chisel handle: one is designed to be struck with a hammer, the other is pushed with the hand. Both are fixed to the blade in a similar fashion (Fig 9.6). The handle that is designed to be struck has a metal hoop at the top of the handle, which must be properly fitted (Fig 9.7).

Sharpening is best carried out using Japanese water stones. Because the bulk of the blade is made from soft steel it is very quickly abraded away. The very hard steel face of the tool forms the cutting

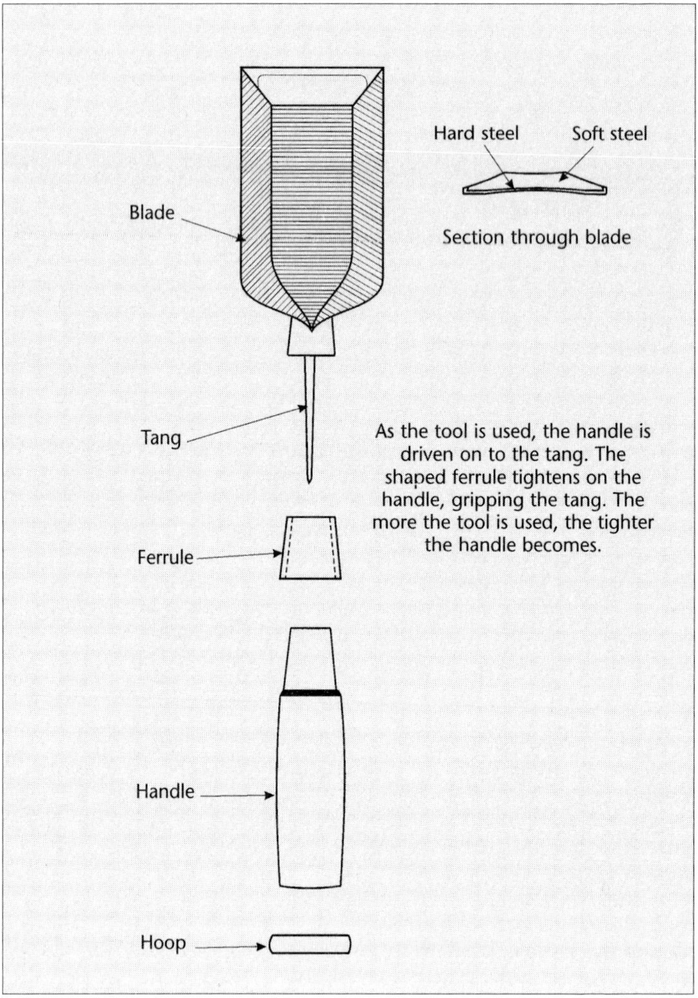

Fig 9.6 Japanese chisel assembly.

edge. Four stones of 800, 1,200, 6,000 and 8,000 grit size are useful, though the first two are only used when the edge is in very poor condition. Some craftsmen use double bevels similar to that on a Western chisel. I use a single bevel that varies according to the type of work for which the chisel is used. The thin finishing chisels (*Usu-nomi*) are sharpened at about 27° while the short butt chisels (*Oire-nomi*) have an angle of 30° (Fig 9.8).

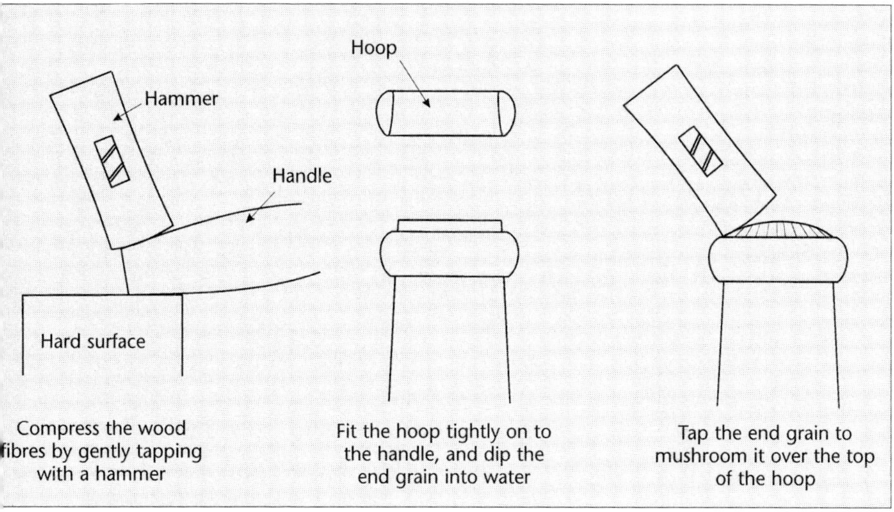

Fig 9.7 Fitting the hoop on a Japanese chisel handle.

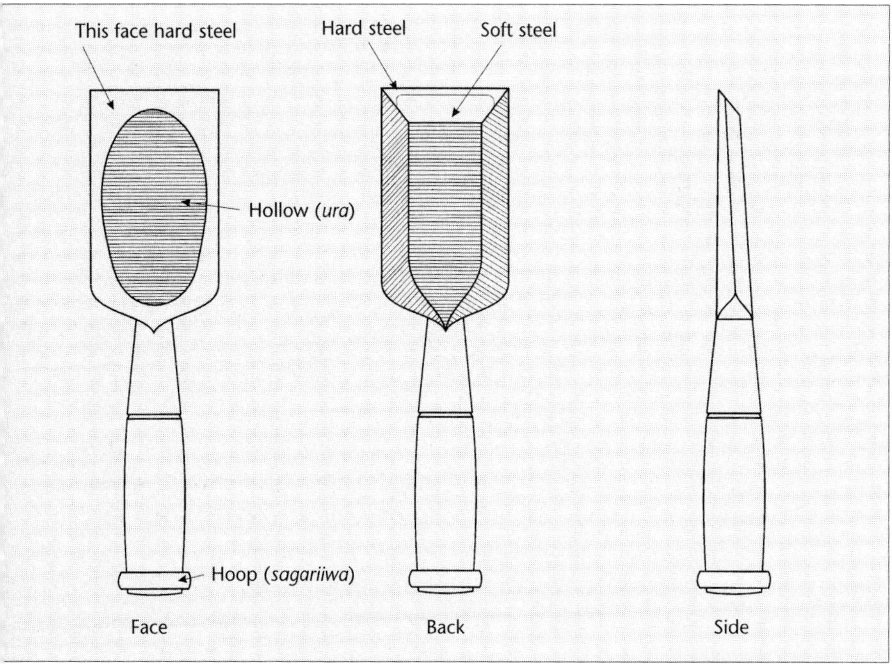

Fig 9.8 Japanese butt chisel (*Oire-nomi*).

CHAPTER 10

Gouges

The Cannel

The ground angle forming the cutting edge of a gouge is called the cannel. When the bevel is on the outside, as on a firmer gouge, the tool is described as 'out cannel'. When on the inside, as that of a scribing gouge, it is referred to as 'in cannel'. Out-cannel tools are easier to sharpen than in-cannel. This applies particularly to grinding the bevel. Some grinding machines can be fitted with a gouge cone, which is useful, but because the part of the cone that is most frequently used is of small diameter, the surface speed is well below the optimum. This makes grinding a laborious process. Small grinding points that will fit into the chuck of an electric drill can be used. These work fairly well, but be very careful not to grind the cutting edge out of shape. There is also the heat problem when dry grinding. The tool needs to be frequently cooled to prevent the steel's temper from being spoilt. Honing the in-cannel gouge requires shaped stones, which were discussed in Chapter 5.

Firmer Gouges

The firmer gouge is sharpened out-cannel. It is frequently used with a mallet to remove large quantities of wood, so the edge needs to be robust. Some firmer gouges have a bent blade and a hoop on the top of the handle. These tools are intended for heavy work, and are sharpened with a steep cutting bevel. Firmer gouges are obtainable in sizes from 3⁄16in (5mm) to 2in (51mm). The length of the cutting edge of a 1in gouge is about 2¾in (70mm) long, and to put a good edge on this requires a lot of work. Whether the tool is rubbed along the stone in a lengthwise movement or at right angles to the stone (Figs 10.1a and b), the whole length of the cutting edge needs the same amount of attention. This means the tool must be rolled as it moves along the stone, so it is difficult to keep the honing bevel flat on the stone. It is very easy to round the bevel, and if this happens the tool will never be properly sharp. Gouges are usually sharpened with a single bevel, that is to say, there are no separate honing and grinding bevels. Once the outside bevel has been honed the edge is finished by removing any internal burr with a slip stone. Keep the slip flat inside the gouge – there must be no bevel on the inside.

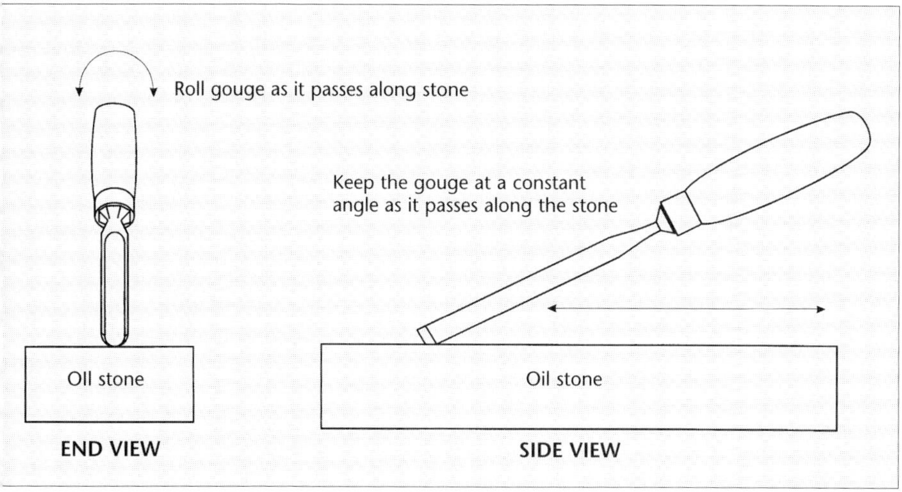

Fig 10.1a Honing a firmer gouge.

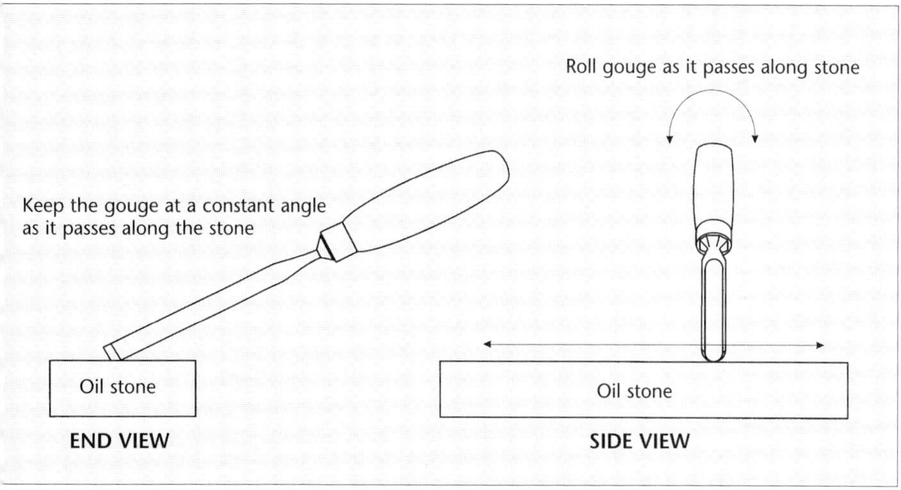

Fig 10.1b Alternative method of honing a firmer gouge.

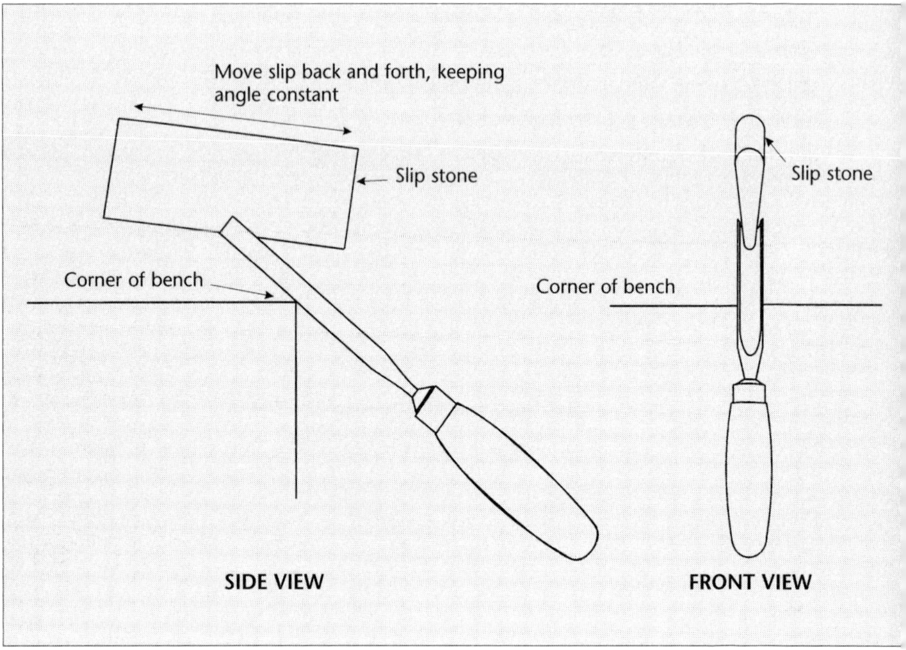

Fig 10.2 Honing a scribing gouge.

Scribing Gouges

The scribing gouge is usually a more delicate tool than most firmer gouges. Its main task is to scribe intersecting mouldings and, as this means cutting across end grain, the edge must be really keen. Unless working in hardwood, which would require a stout edge, an included angle of about 27° will be found most suitable. It is extremely difficult to keep the bevel flat inside the gouge. There are two ways that the bevel can be honed. The slip can be held in the vice, with the required round uppermost, and the tool rubbed on it, though it is difficult to see what is happening to the cutting edge. Alternatively, hold the tool across the edge of the bench and rub the slip on the bevel. In this way it is possible to keep the bevel constant throughout its entire length (Fig 10.2). The most useful scribing gouges are those with a deep sweep, though these are the most difficult to sharpen.

Carving Gouges

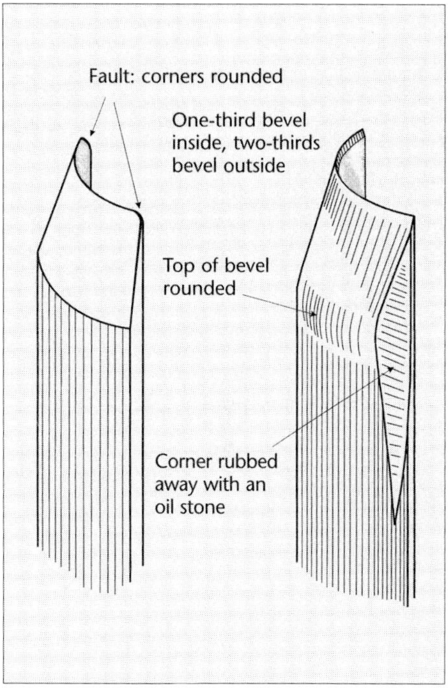

Fig 10.3 Cutting edge of a carving gouge.

This section deals only with gouges – fluters and veiners are covered in Chapter 11. Most carvers sharpen their gouges with bevels both inside and out, usually in the proportion of two-thirds outside and one-third inside. The tool can then be used curved side up or down.

There are two unique features often used when sharpening carving gouges. The corner on the side of the gouge is rubbed away on the oil stone (Fig 10.3), which allows the tool to make a thin cut right into an acute corner. The hard corner on the outside of the gouge where the bevel meets the back of the tool is rounded, which allows the tool to make a controlled scoop cut (Fig 10.4). When sharpening any carving tool it is important to preserve the ears, that is, the corners of the cutting edge. If these important parts of the cutting edge are lost the effective length and shape of the tool is reduced (Fig 10.3). The included angle at the cutting edge varies with the work being undertaken: a gouge used for boosting out hardwood might be as steep as 32°, while a gouge used for finishing cuts on a piece of lime would work best at 27°. Carving gouges are made with the blade shaped lengthwise. As well as straight there are bent tools, forward bent being the most often used. These are more difficult to sharpen than the straight, but the edge configuration is the same. Spoons are particularly difficult, as there is little room for the slip to be rubbed back and forth. Acutely bent spoons are best sharpened with a stone file that can be rolled on the bevel. Because of the difficulty in servicing these tools they are only used when absolutely necessary. All carving tools need to be super sharp. The edge is usually finished and quite often maintained by stropping (see Chapter 6).

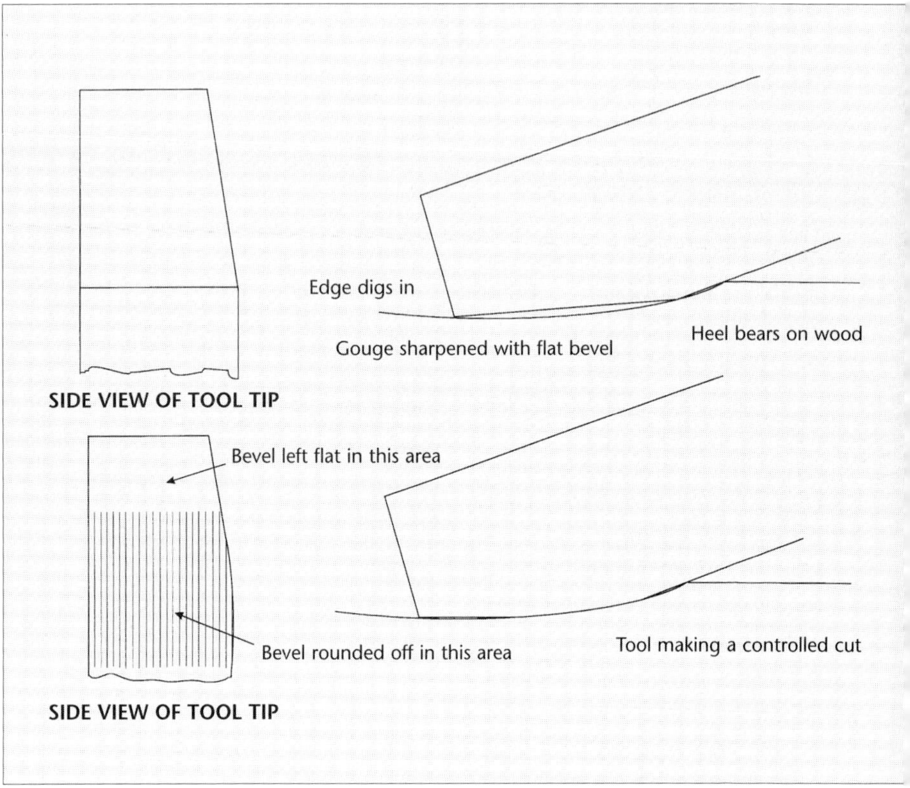

Fig 10.4 How the bevel shape affects the cut made.

Turning Gouges

The long and strong roughing-out gouge used for between centres turning has a U-shaped section, the most commonly used size being ¾in (19mm). This tool has a cutting edge 1¼in (32mm) long that must be kept straight and 90° to the length of the tool. The included angle of the edge is 45°. The cutting edge on all carving tools must be formed by a single bevel. This bevel must be flat, that is, neither hollow nor rounded (Fig 10.5).

Spindle gouges have a shallow section and are usually sharpened with their end resembling the shape of a finger nail. The bevel is flatter than that of the roughing out gouge. An included angle of

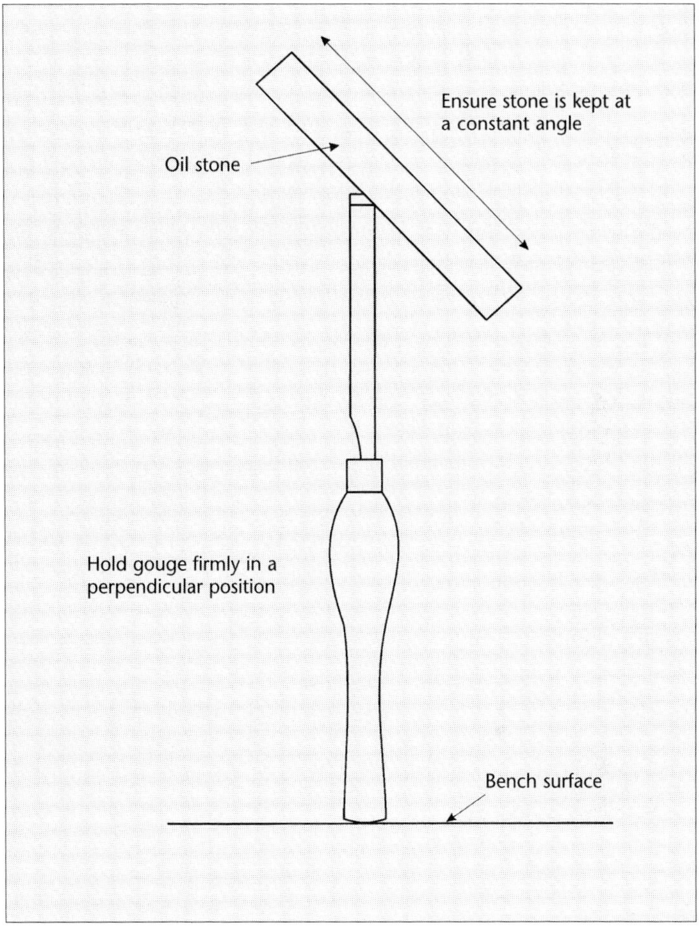

Fig 10.5 Honing a turning gouge.

30° to 35° is suitable.

Bowl gouges have a very deep U-shaped section. There are varying opinions among turners as to the best shape for the end of this tool. I sharpen my tools with the end straight across at 90° to the length. The bevel is sharpened at 40°.

Honing turning tools is difficult because of their length. The easiest way is to stand the tool vertically on its handle and rub the bevel with the stone. Any burr formed on the inside must be removed with a slip stone (Fig 10.6).

Paring Gouges

Paring gouges are mainly used by pattern-makers, but they are useful tools in any workshop. They are made to cut a true segment of a circle, which is known as the sweep of the gouge. For instance, a 6in (152mm) sweep would cut a segment of 6in diameter. They are in-cannel tools, the outside of the blade's section forming the sweep. The paring gouge is never driven with a mallet, as it is a light precision tool. As very few new paring gouges are made, old ones are valued. It is important that the correct sweep is maintained. Large sweeps of 10in (254mm) and over are very difficult to sharpen, as it is hard to keep the cutting edge straight on these large sweeps. It is often necessary to grind the end square and reform the cannel. Most pattern-making is done in a mild timber, so a low-angled cutting edge of 25° is quite normal. A deep gouge of about 1in (25mm) sweep is often used for removing the bulk of waste wood from a job, and in this case an angle nearer to 30° would be appropriate. Cranked paring gouges are treated in a similar way to straight gouges.

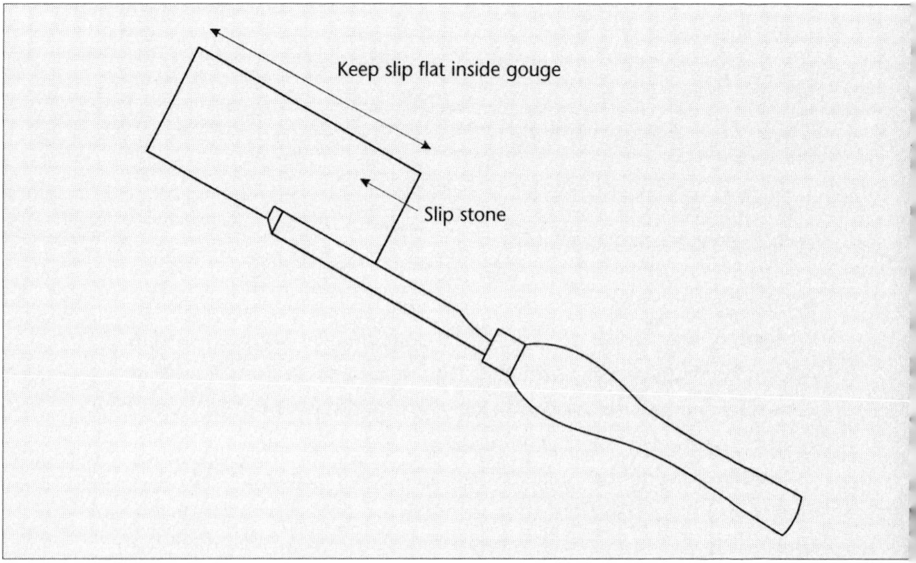

Fig 10.6 Removing the burr from the inside of a gouge.

CHAPTER 11

Special-shaped Tools

In Chapters 9 and 10 I described sharpening flat cutting edges (chisels) and curved cutting edges (gouges). All other shaped edges are a combination of these two (Fig 11.1). While either flat or curved shapes are comparatively easy to sharpen on their own, there are problems when they are combined. Most tools require the cutting edge to be straight, that is, if the tool were stabbed into a piece of wood all of the cut made would be to the same depth, and this is particularly important when sharpening carving tools.

Parting Tools

The parting tool is sometimes referred to as the 'V' tool, which is probably a better description. The angle formed by the two cutting edges varies from 90° to 30°. The wider the angle and the bigger the tool, the easier it is to sharpen. Care must be taken to keep the edge at 90° to the length of the tool. A common problem is that a beak forms where the two flat blades meet, which is caused by the small

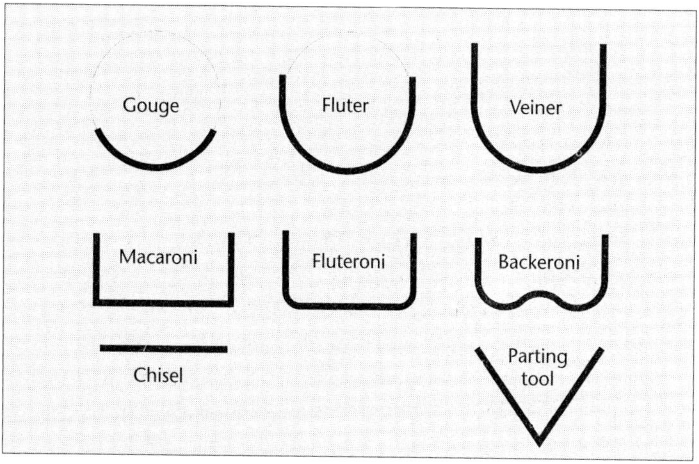

Fig 11.1 Sections of carving tools.

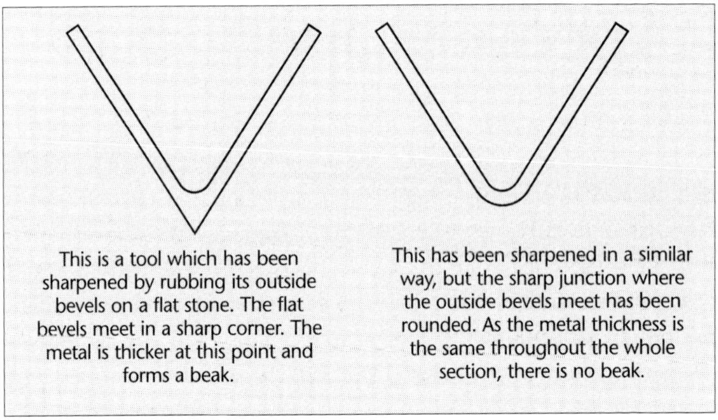

Fig 11.2 Sections of the cutting end of parting tools.

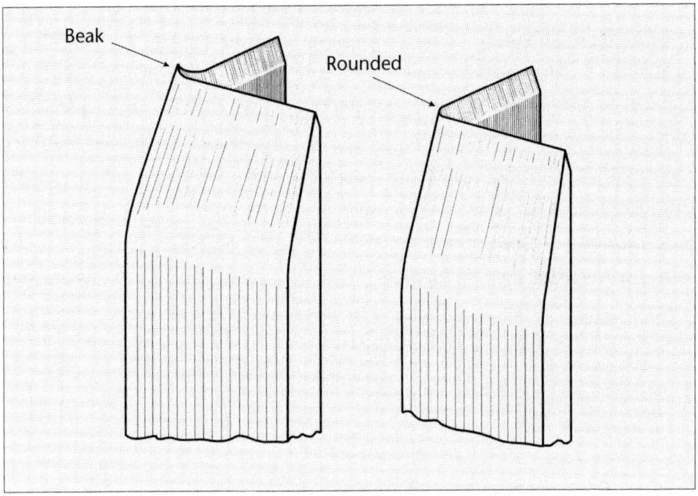

Fig 11.3 Tip of a parting tool.

radius inside the tool (Fig 11.2) as the section of the tool is thicker at this point. The beak is removed by forming a small radius on the outside to the tool. Unless both outside flat surfaces are sharpened the same amount the cutting edge becomes deformed (Fig 11.3). Parting tools used for lettering usually have the bevel inside the tool. The most convenient tool to hone this internal bevel is the diamond-plated shim. This gets right down into the intersection, which is almost impossible with a slip.

Bruzze or Corner Chisels

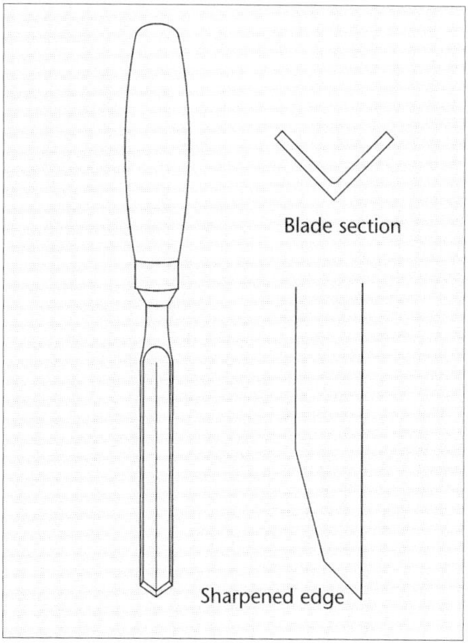

Fig 11.4 The bruzze.

There are several varieties of this tool. The wheelwright's bruzze is a large tool, each wing of the blade being as wide as 1in (25mm). The bruzze is used for cleaning the corners of mortises, so the outside of the blades must be flat (Fig 11.4). The cutting edge is formed by bevels inside the tool, and for most work the included angle of the bevel is 30°. It is possible, if great care is taken, to grind these bevels. It is thus possible to have separate grinding and honing bevels, which makes sharpening less arduous than working with a single bevel. A small corner chisel with blades ⅜in (9mm) wide is a useful cabinet-making tool. A honing angle somewhat flatter than that on the wheelwright's bruzze should be applied. The bevel will be dependent on the type of wood being worked: 27° is suitable for hardwoods.

The Veiner

If you look at the section of this tool in Fig 11.1 you will see that it can be treated as two flat blades joined by a curved blade. The veiner is sharpened with a bevel on the outside (there is no bevel on the inside). The tool can be honed on a flat bench stone. The outside of one of the flat portions is rubbed with a single stroke on the stone. The tool is then rolled for two strokes to hone the curved part, and finally the other flat has one stroke on the stone. Keep the angle of the tool constant throughout the whole of the sharpening process. Be careful to keep the cutting edge straight. It pays to stop honing every few strokes and inspect the edge, as there is a tendency to remove too much metal from the ears of the blade. If this happens it may be necessary to grind the end of the tool square and reform the bevel. The angle of the bevel will vary according to the wood being worked. This is explained in the paragraph headed 'Carving Chisels' in Chapter 9. Any burr formed on the inside of the tool should be cleaned off with slip stones.

The Fluter

This carving tool is treated in exactly the same way as the veiner. It is formed in the same way by two flat cutting edges connected by a curved cutting edge, though in this case the two flat cutting edges are shorter. This makes the tool easier to sharpen.

The Macaroni, Fluteroni and Backeroni

These carving tools are all sharpened with a bevel on the inside (Fig 11.1). The macaroni have small radii inside where the flat blades meet. These form a beak similar to that described above for the parting tool. It is dealt with in exactly the same way, by rounding the outside corner of the intersection. This rounding should be treated with caution as the outside shape of the tool is most important. Keep the outside radii as small as possible.

The fluteroni is similar to the macaroni except that the corners are formed by a curved cutting edge, so there are three flat surfaces joined by two curved cutting edges. All of these have to be sharpened from the inside of the tool. Shaped slip stones are used, and the tool takes time to sharpen. Most craftsmen only use the fluteroni when no other tool will do the job, and they try to keep the sharpening of it as infrequent as possible. All that has been said about the fluteroni applies to the backeroni.

Draw Lock Chisels

Sharpening the draw lock chisel is relatively easy. There are two varieties of this tool. A single, all-metal tool with a blade at each end is the most common (Fig 11.5), though cabinet-makers prefer the type that consists of two separate tools. The cutting edge of the blades on each tool are set at 90° to one another. The edge is configured exactly

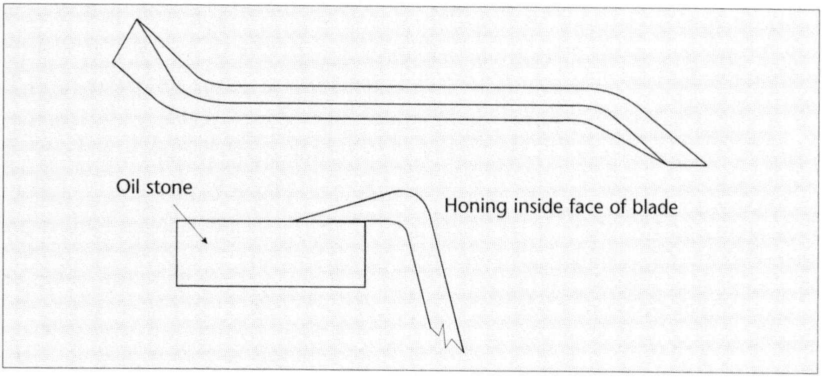

Fig 11.5 All-metal draw lock chisel.

the same as a normal woodworking chisel, flat on one side and bevelled on the other. The cutting edge which is set at 90° to the length of the tool has to be honed on a stone that is not set in a box.

Chequering Tool

This tool, used mainly by gun stockers, deviates from the sharpening techniques previously described, and you need to fully understand the way the tool works before any attempt is made to sharpen it. The cutting edge is formed from hardened steel, and a medium-grade slip stone is used to sharpen the teeth. Before starting to sharpen the tool, carefully inspect the teeth. The teeth on one side are lower than

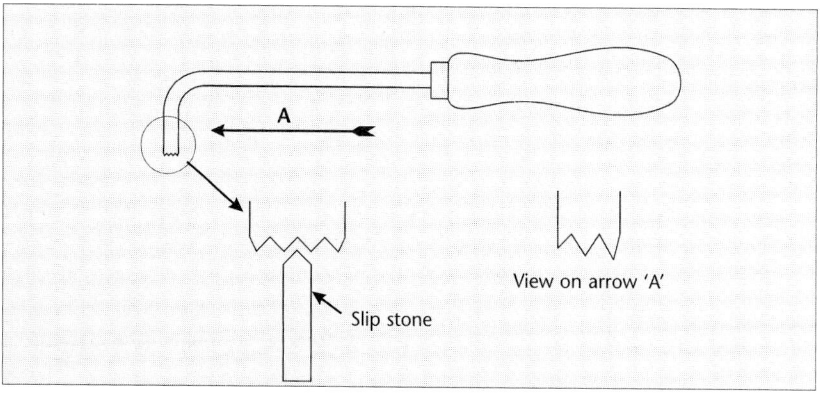

Fig 11.6 Chequering tool.

the other, and it is important that this configuration is maintained (Fig 11.6). Use a slip stone that has been shaped to fit in the 'V' between the teeth. Shaping a slip stone specially for this purpose is usually necessary. Use a piece of aluminium oxide paper fixed on a hard, flat surface and rub the slip on this. Carefully pass the slip stone along each 'V' in turn. Keep the tips of the teeth even. A watch-maker's lens is useful for this task.

Centre Punch

The centre punch is a metalworking tool, but it is often used by woodworkers. The point must be shaped at the correct angle and at the same time formed centrally. Freehand grinding of the point is normal practice (Fig 11.7). The tool is rolled as the point is ground, which is made easier if a block of metal with a 'V' filed in it is clamped to the tool rest. The punch fits into the 'V' which keeps it at the correct angle to the grinding wheel. An included angle of 90° is used to mark a point in which to start a drill. If the punch is used to set out on plate metal an included angle of 60° is used.

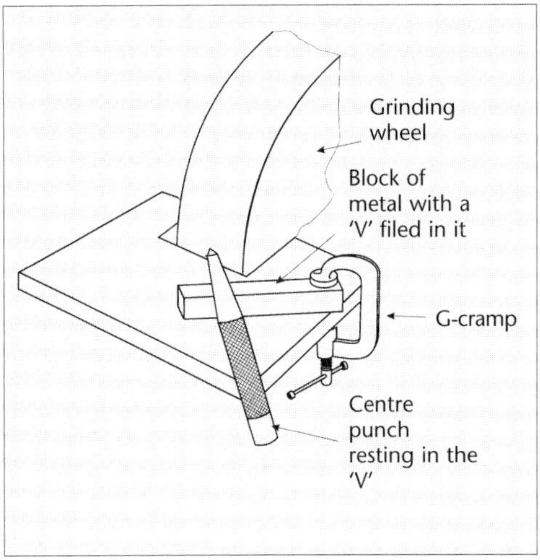

Fig 11.7 Grinding the point on a centre punch.

Screwdrivers

The screwdriver is not a cutting tool, but its edge still needs reshaping from time to time. This is usually referred to as sharpening. The end should be a perfect fit in the screw's slot or the latter becomes deformed, which makes it not only unsightly but difficult to extract. This refers only to the normal screwdriver used on slotted screws – there is no way of refurbishing drivers for Phillips or cross-point screws. Commercially made screwdrivers have their tip formed by two flat faces ground at an angle to one another, resulting in a wedge-shaped tip. As pressure is applied to turn the screw the driver thus tends to rise out of the slot. A tip formed by parallel faces is far more effective (Fig 11.8). Screwdriver blades are softer than cutting tools. The metal can therefore be filed, which is often a better proposition than grinding as there is less chance of overheating the metal and spoiling the temper. You will also have more control over the file.

Dividers and Compasses

These tools, used for marking circles and marking off dimensions, are fairly easy to sharpen, as the metal from which they are made is soft when compared with woodcutting tools. However, they should not necessarily be filed: unless the tool has sustained accidental damage a medium oil stone is the only tool required to restore the point. Close the points until they touch each other, and rub both sides of the points on the stone. Then, with the points still together, rub the outside of each point with the stone. The outside of each point is rounded. Make sure that both points are of equal length.

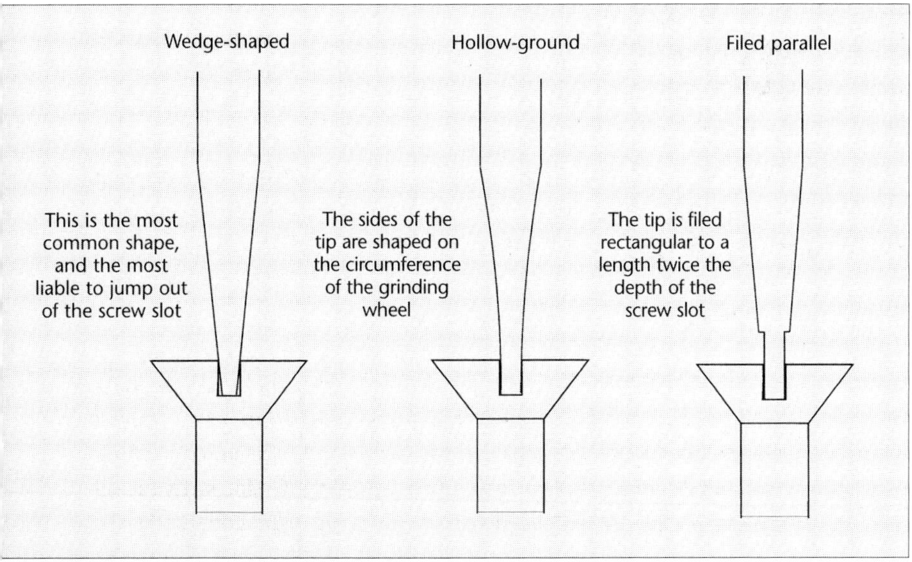

Fig 11.8 Screwdriver tips.

CHAPTER 12

Sharpening and Setting Saws

Not only are there saws for different purposes, there is also a wide range of qualities. In recent years disposable saws have become available which have inductance-hardened teeth so hard that it is impossible to file them. However, a quality saw which can be sharpened is easily kept in peak condition.

A saw needs to have the correct tooth configuration (Fig 12.1). If you are able to sharpen a saw you can alter the tooth shape to suit the type of work you do. If you follow the instructions and study the illustrations in this chapter you should, with a little practice, be able to keep your saws in tip-top condition.

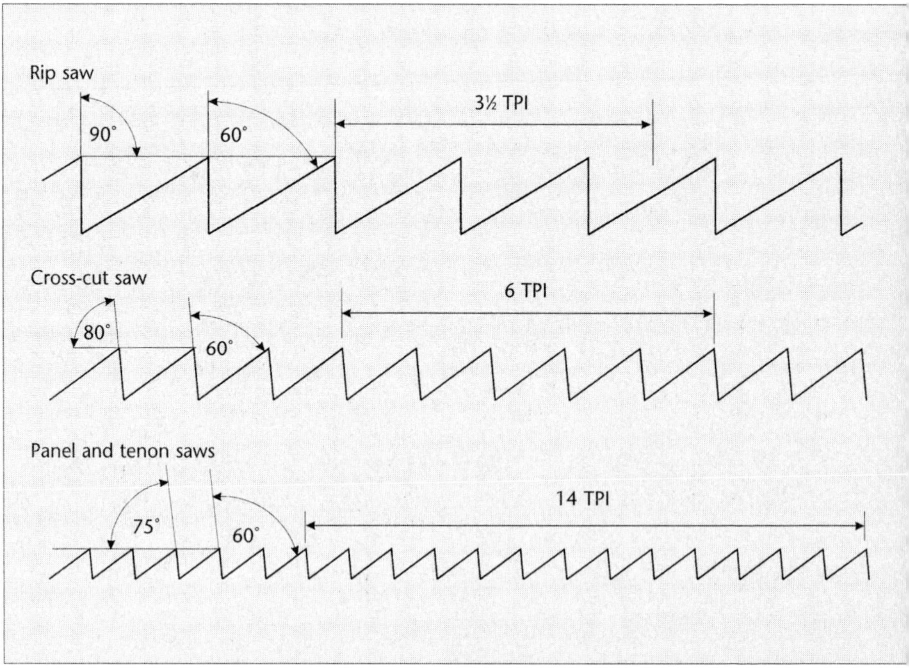

Fig 12.1 Suggested saw-tooth configuration.

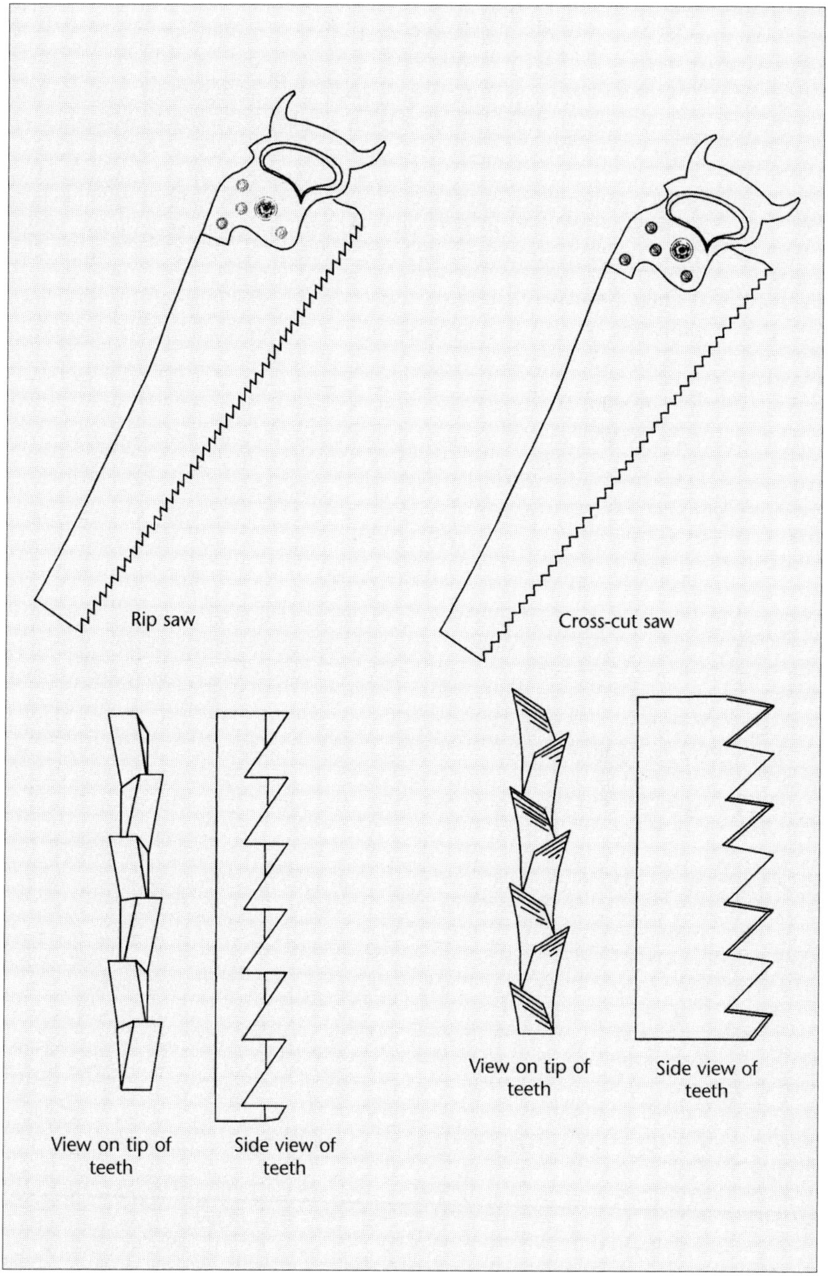

Fig 12.2 The teeth of a rip saw and a cross-cut saw.

Tooth Configuration

The shape and size of the saw's teeth is determined by the task the saw will be used for, which is best understood if we first look at the structure of a piece of wood. When cutting across the grain a knife-like action is needed. Every fibre has to be severed in two places and a piece of thickness of the saw removed, which allows the saw room to pass through and cut the fibres below. When cutting along the length, only the fibres in the path of the saw have to be removed, and this is accomplished by using a chisel-like action. Ideally, a different tooth shape is needed for each of these tasks (Fig 12.2).

The thickness of the saw has a profound effect on the way the saw cuts. The cut has to be wide enough to allow the saw free passage, so the thicker the saw the wider the saw cut, or kerf. As all the wood from the kerf has to be removed some manual effort is involved – the wider the kerf the more is the effort required to saw the same distance. As nearly all saws cut on the push stroke, the saw has to be stiff enough to remain straight during the cutting stroke, and most of the stiffness in handsaws is obtained from the thickness of the blade. Japanese saws, however, cut on the pull stroke. When the blade is cutting it is

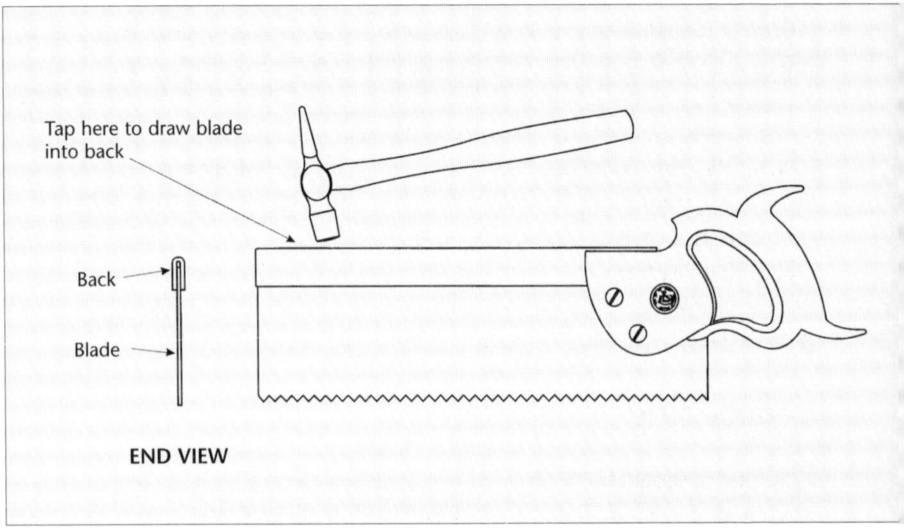

Fig 12.3 Tensioning a backsaw.

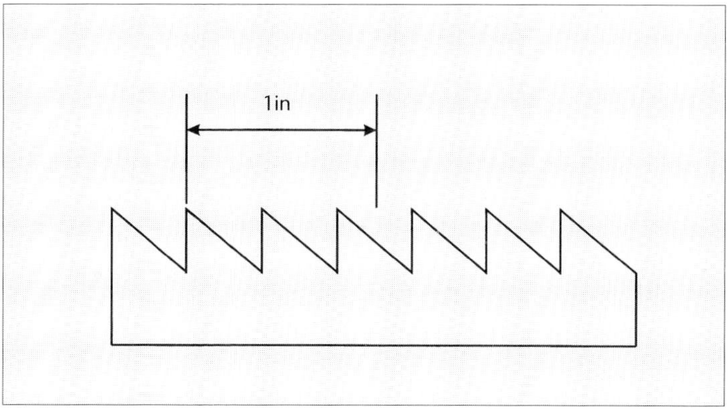

Fig 12.4 Part of a rip saw blade with 3½ teeth per inch.

in tension and this action keeps the blade straight. Japanese saws are very thin and cut much faster than the thick Western saws. Backsaws are thinner than saws with an unsupported blade.

The blade of the backsaw is tensioned. The edge of the blade held by the back is longer than the cutting edge, and this back keeps the long edge straight. The back is just a piece of thick metal bent over the top of the blade. After long use the blade tends to come out of the back. As the back gets nearer to coming off the tension in the blade is reduced, and the cutting edge takes on a sideways curve. A smart tap on the top of the back draws the blade into the back, and any curvature of the blade is cured (Fig 12.3).

The size of the teeth are specified by the number of points per inch (TPI), all the teeth contained in one inch being counted (Fig 12.4). This figure varies from 3½ TPI for a full rip saw to 24 TPI on a fine dovetail saw. The size of hand saws ranges from a blade length of 30in (762mm) on a full rip to 20in (508mm) on a panel saw. Backsaws have a large size range: a full carcass saw's blade can be as long as 20in (508mm) while that of a small jeweller's saw is only 4in (102mm) long.

Sharpening the Teeth

All the teeth should be the same size, except on the tip of the ripsaw where they are graduated. It is very easy to file the teeth so that there is one large tooth followed by a small tooth all the way down the

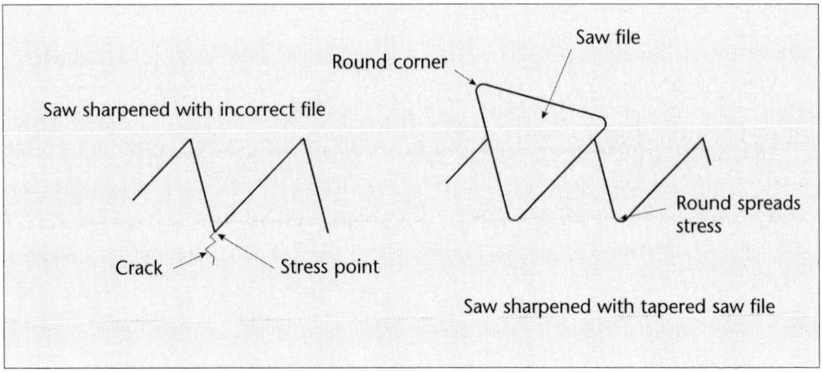

Fig 12.5 The importance of using the correct file for sharpening a saw.

saw (known as cows and calves). Sighting along the teeth of the saw, they should be in a straight line or in a gentle arched curve – never must the cutting edge be allowed to become concave. When a saw has a concave cutting edge, each successive tooth stands a little higher than the preceding one, which induces a shuddering action as the saw cuts, and the saw is difficult to control. The height of the teeth on both sides of the saw must be identical, or the saw will lead towards the highest side.

If the teeth have become misshapen it is quite easy to reshape them before sharpening. If you are about to sharpen a saw for the first time, try your skill on a saw that is not important. Start on a saw with fairly big teeth, say 6 TPI or less.

Saw files are a special sort of file. They are triangular in section and have tapered blades. There are two different designs: single and double ended. The double ended is easiest to use as its length provides more control. The size of the file is determined by the tooth size of the saw. The tooth should not occupy more than two-thirds of the file's side (Fig 12.5), but the file must not be much larger than this or you will not be able to see the tooth being filed.

Holding the Saw

The saw must be held securely while it is being filed, and the blade held rigid so that the file does not cause any chatter. Two workshop-made appliances are used for this purpose (Figs 12.6 and 12.7).

There are also proprietary metal saw vices, but the workshop-made devices work best. One essential for saw sharpening is good light. Natural daylight in front of a window is ideal, as the light shines across the teeth and reflects off the newly filed surfaces.

Sharpening procedures vary with the condition of the saw, but whatever the condition the first task is topping, sometimes called jointing. A flat file is passed along the saw's edge, taking the very tips off all the teeth. This ensures that all the teeth are the same height. If the teeth are badly out of shape some will have larger flats than the others. These teeth are filed to shape so that they match the rest, which is known as 'shaping'. A saw in very poor condition may require a lot of shaping, but this is unusual.

Next, the teeth must be set, that is, bending each tooth so that it

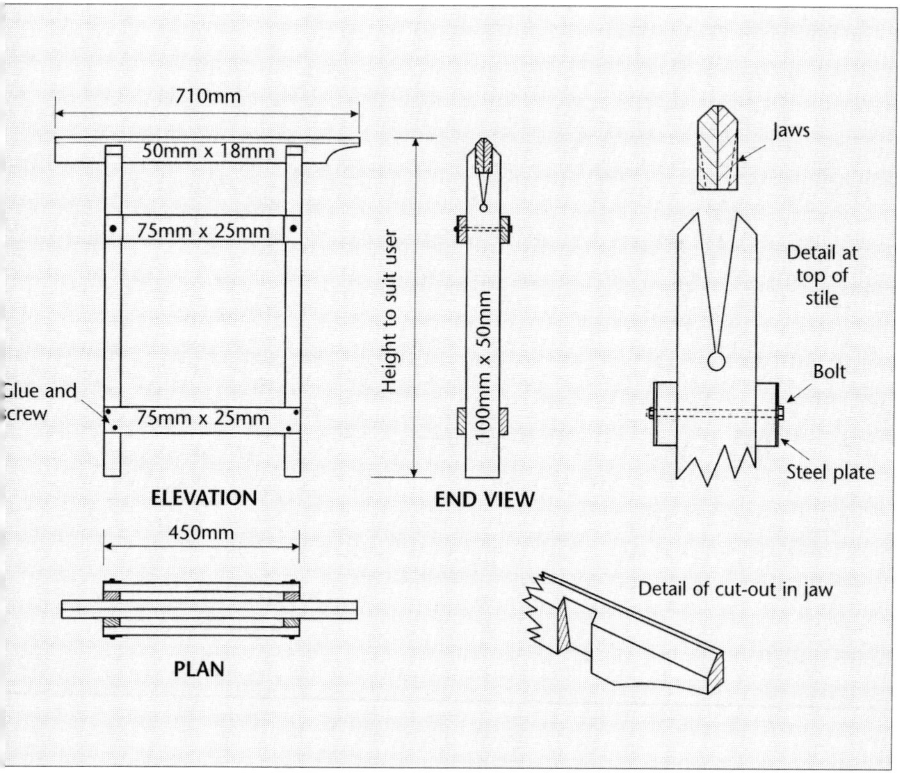

Fig 12.6 Saw-sharpening block.

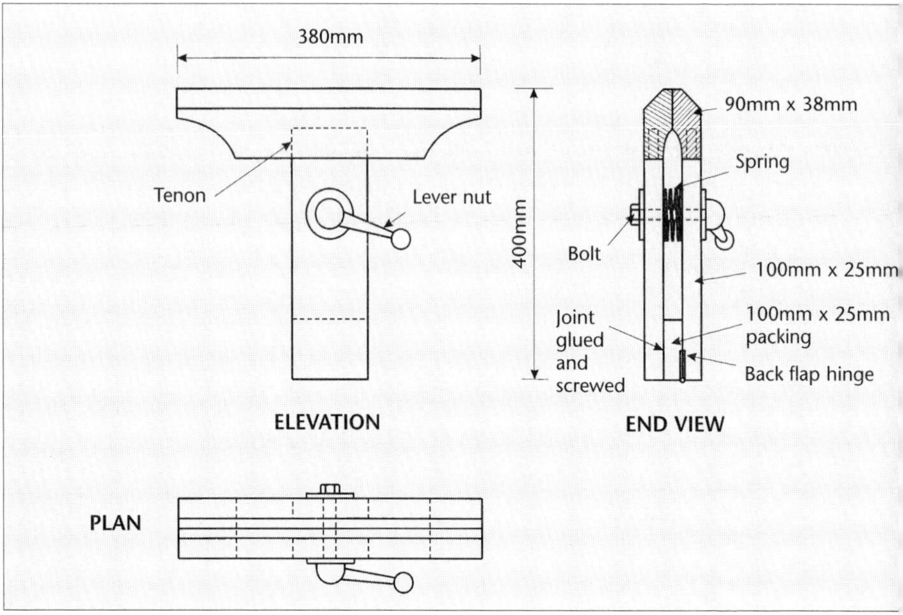

Fig 12.7 Saw-sharpening chops.

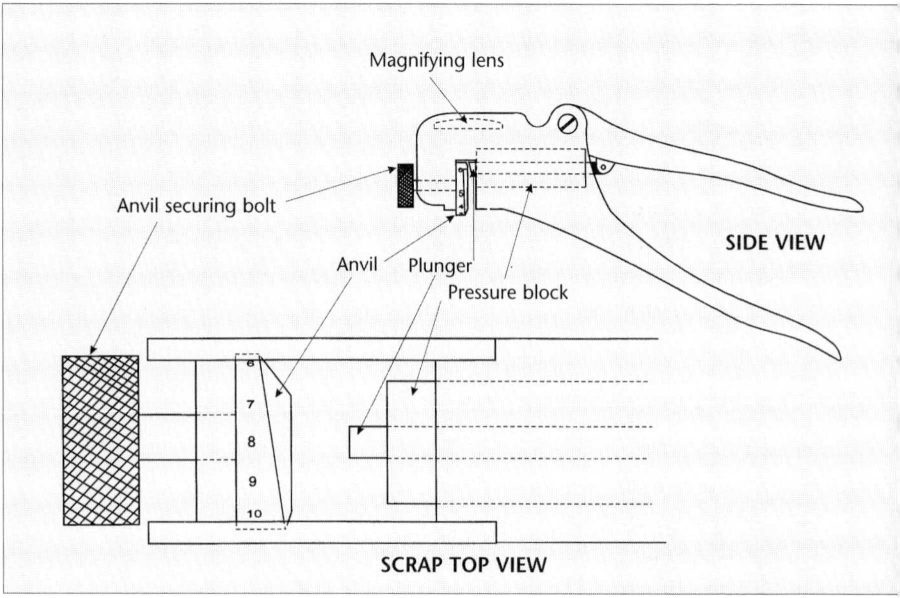

Fig 12.8 Pliers saw set.

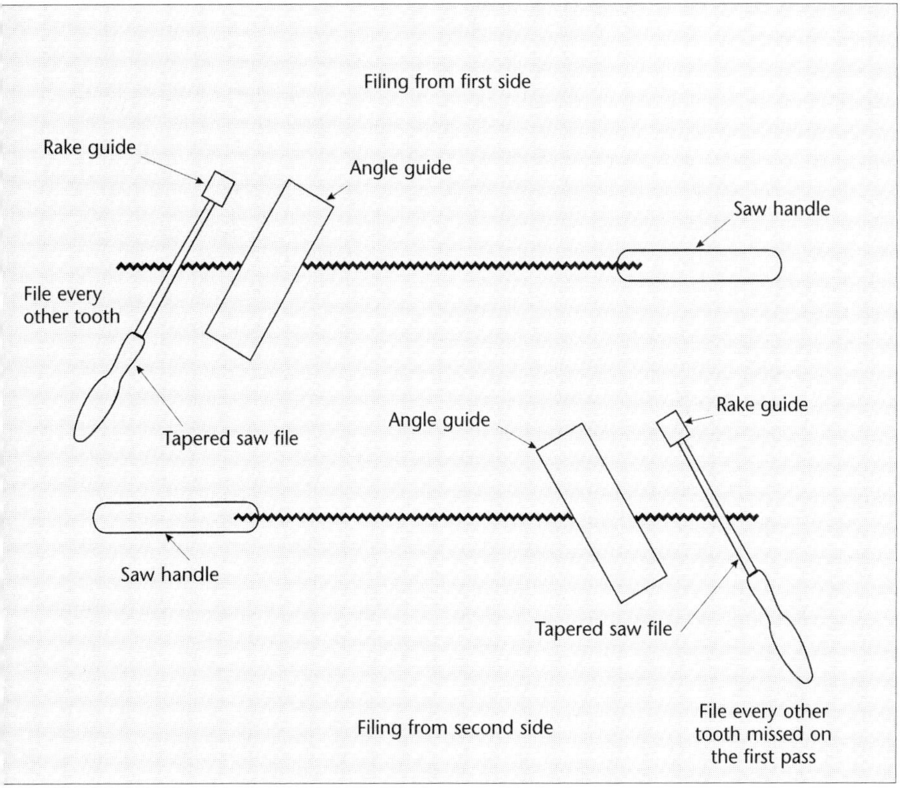

Fig 12.9 Filing a cross-cut saw using guides.

cuts a little wider than the thickness of the saw's blade. This gives the blade clearance in the kerf. The amount of set depends on the wood the saw will be used to cut. Wet timber needs more set than dry timber, and most softwoods need more set than hardwoods. Try to work with as little set as possible on the saw. The wider the kerf the more effort required to make the cut.

Several different tools can be used for this task, the most common being the pliers saw set (Fig 12.8). This tool has a small anvil with a tapered bevel round its edge. The anvil can be set so that the required bevel is opposite a plunger. The tool is placed over the saw tooth and the plunger operated so that it bends the tooth to fit the anvil's bevel. Set the teeth in the same direction as they were originally set, alternate teeth being bent the same way.

Filing or Sharpening

It is extremely difficult to keep the file at the correct angle, so you need some sort of guide. There are several designs on the market, though simple blocks of wood work better than anything that can be bought (Figs 12.9 and 12.10). The saw file cuts on the push stroke – lift it clear of the tooth on the return. Apply very little pressure to the file. Start by filing the tooth furthest from the handle, the gullet of each alternate tooth being filed in turn until the small flat tip of the tooth, produced by topping, is just removed. When all the teeth have been filed the saw is laid flat on the bench and an oil stone is gently rubbed along both sides of the teeth. This removes the rag left by the file, and also ensures that all the teeth have equal set.

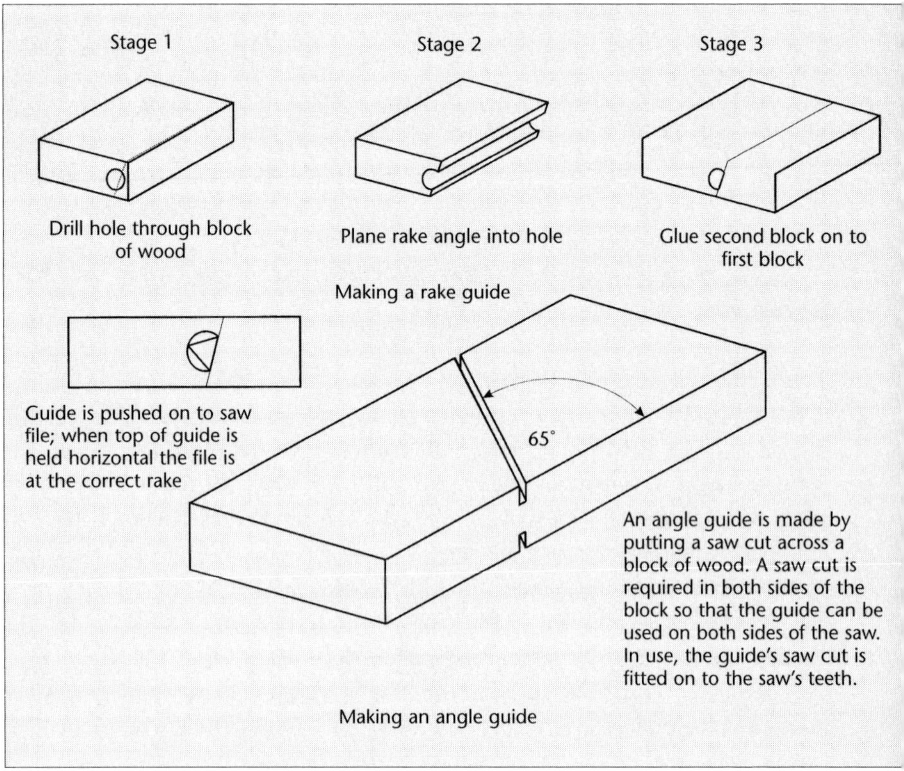

Fig 12.10 Rake and angle guides.

CHAPTER 13

Hole-boring Tools

Woodworkers generally use bits to bore a hole in wood, while engineers use drills to drill a hole in metal. However, when woodworkers use twist drills the process is referred to as drilling a hole. The tools can be divided into two groups: those which have a screw which draws them into the wood, and those that require pressure to make them cut. The screw part of bits needs very careful treatment. There is no spare metal in the screw and any filing detracts from the ideal configuration.

Apart from the drills made to cut metal, all the other hole-making tools are formed from fairly soft steel that can be filed, which makes sharpening less arduous. However, because the soft metal can be freely filed away it is easy to overdo the process and spoil the configuration of the tool.

The tools needed for sharpening bits are few. Saw files that have been used for sharpening saws become blunt on the rounded corners and are no longer suitable for saw sharpening, but are ideal for sharpening bits. Small stone files can be used to make a keen cutting edge. The round file sold for sharpening chain saw blades is ideal for Gedge and solid-nosed bits.

Flat Wood Bits

The flat bit is a low-cost simple tool made for the DIY market. It is, however, quite effective, and a useful tool. It is very basic, and sharpening could not be simpler. The centre point around which the two cutting faces rotate has three faces. Keep these faces flat and make sure the point remains in the centre of the cutting circle, or the tool will not cut an accurate hole. The edge of the two cutting faces is sharpened at an angle. Keep the original angle when sharpening. Unless the tool is damaged by hitting a hidden nail or screw it will only require minor treatment, a small stone being the best tool for this. After the cutting bevels have been honed, rub both sides of the tool flat on a stone to remove any burr.

Centre Bits

This very useful tool is, unfortunately, no longer made in its original flat form, though many are still in use. There are several different patterns. Modern versions have a centre screw and a half helical turn like the end of an auger bit. The flat type of centre bit is dealt with here. The other version is treated in the same way as an auger bit. There are three items that require attention: the point, nicker and cutter (Fig 13.1). The point is formed by three flat faces, which are easily filed, but care should be taken to ensure that the point's position is maintained. Any deviation from the original position alters the diameter of the hole being bored. The nicker forms the side of the hole, so its cutting edge must have clearance bevels. The cut made by the nicker is slightly outside the

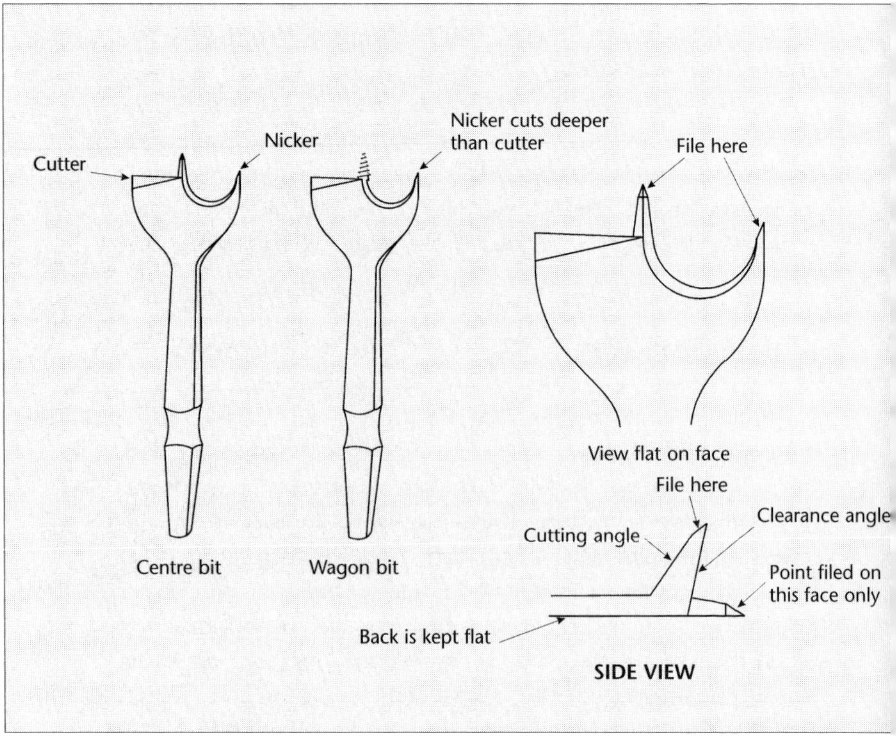

Fig 13.1 Centre bits.

circle scribed by the cutter. The cutter's blade has a clearance angle on the underside. Most centre bits are made of soft metal, so filing should be undertaken with care; a stone is the least less aggressive tool to use.

Shell and Spoon Bits

The shell bit resembles the blade of a gouge, and is so similar that it is sometimes, known as a 'gouge bit' (Fig 13.2). The cutting end is sharpened with a single outside bevel of 30°. The edge is straight and at 90° to the length of the tool. Although it seems logical that the tool would work better with the bevel inside (in cannel), it makes no difference. As the outside bevel is so much easier to form and sharpen it is the best one to use. Sharpen the tool in exactly the same way as described for the in-cannel gouge.

The spoon bit has a blade formed exactly the same as the shell bit, but the cutting edge is different. The edge is formed by the end of the tool being a flat bevel on the hollow side (Fig 13.2).

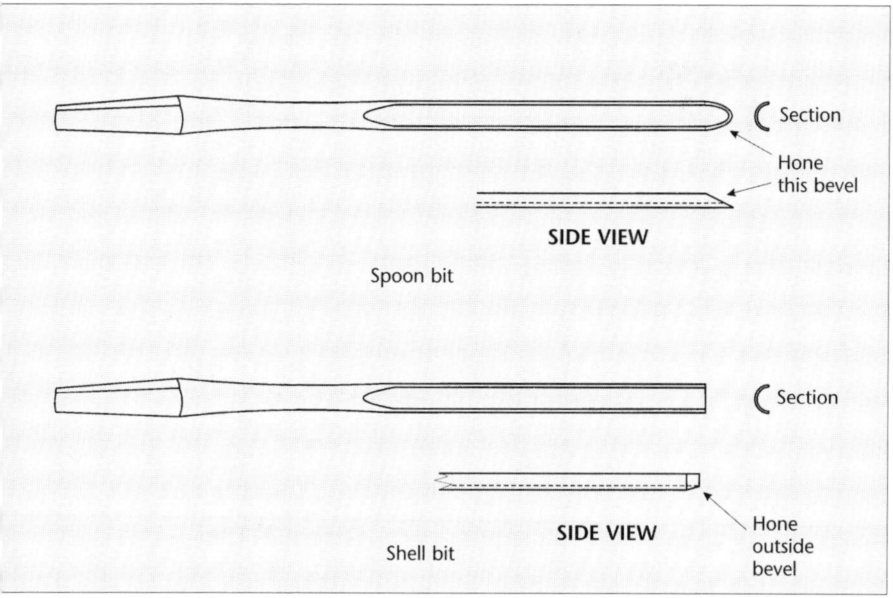

Fig 13.2 Shell and spoon bits.

The tool is rubbed with this bevel flat on the oil stone. The cutting end takes on a rounded configuration. After honing the bevel remove any burr on the outside by rubbing the rounded side of the tool on a stone, rolling the tool as it is rubbed. Be careful to keep the outside straight, do not dub it off at the tip.

Bradawls

A bradawl in good condition is a most useful tool, though it tends to be a mistreated item. Two designs are used by the woodworker. The pointed awl used by leatherworkers is worse than useless for making holes in wood, as the pointed, tapered blade of this tool splits wood. The woodworker's awl has a straight cutting edge, which is formed

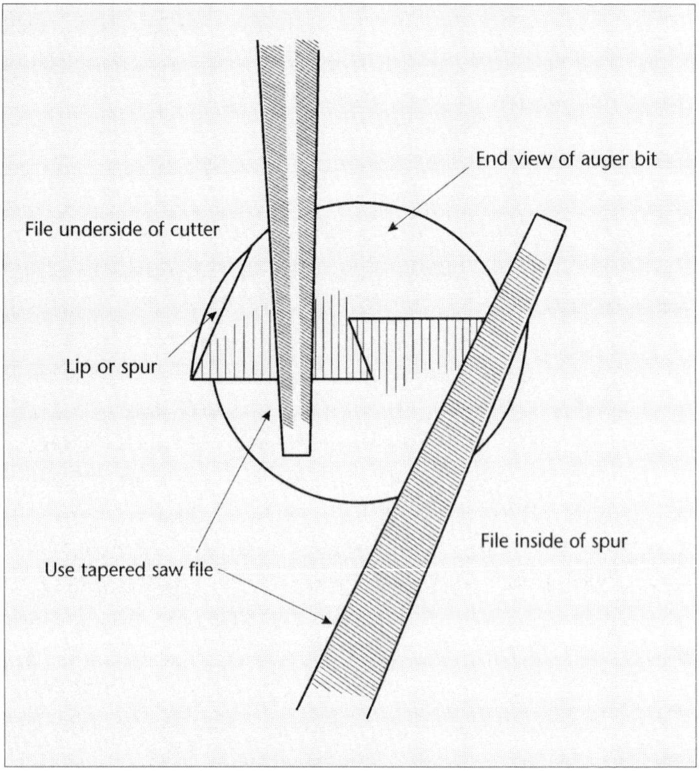

Fig 13.3 Sharpening an auger bit.

by bevels from each side of the blade. The bevels are sharpened by honing similarly to sharpening a chisel. In use the bradawl is placed with the cutting edge at 90° to the wood's grain. Pressure is applied and the tool oscillated a few degrees in each direction. The wood fibres are cut, not forced apart as with a pointed awl.

A tool with a tapered square blade is known as a 'bird cage-maker's awl'. This is a very effective tool. The four corners of the blade cut the wood as the tool is turned in the hole. The tool very seldom needs sharpening. Each side of the blade is rubbed in turn on an oil stone, and the very tip of the tool should terminate in a sharp point.

Half-twist or Gimlet Bit

These tools have never been very popular with serious woodworkers as they have a tendency to split the wood. A round file is used to sharpen the inside of the spiral flute, and a three-cornered stone file is used on the thread at the tip of the tool. The half-twist bit is sometimes known as a 'Swiss bit'.

Auger Bits

The most common designs of auger bit are the Jennings and Irwin patterns, the difference being the spiral that removes the waste from the hole being bored. The Jennings has two spirals and the Irwin has only one. The cutting parts of both bits, however, are the same, so the sharpening techniques are identical (Fig 13.3). A small flat file with a safe edge is the best tool to use for most of the sharpening work. There are two wings, and each has a nicker and a cutter. Nickers should only be sharpened from the inside, while the only treatment given to the outside should be the careful removal of any burr. The cutter has a clearance angle on the underside, the cutting bevel being on the top side. Both these bevels should be dressed with a flat file. When filing the underside, keep the safe edge of the file towards the centre screw. The included cutting bevel is 30°. The underside face of the cutter should go right to the centre and intersect with the top thread of the screw. It is important to keep both cutters the same length. The screw is the most delicate part of the tool; if it becomes damaged it can, if not in too bad a state, be restored with a fine three-cornered needle file. Any filing of the screw should be kept to a minimum.

The auger bits described above must be started at 90° to the surface of the wood, which means that only holes perpendicular to the surface can be bored. The 'solid-nosed' and 'Gedge bits' are designed to overcome this restriction. Study the cutting action of the tool carefully before attempting to sharpen it. A fine-toothed round file is used to sharpen the inside of the cutters. The outside has a clearance angle, which is best formed with a flat file that has a safe edge. The cutting edge is curved round a hole on the solid-nosed bit, and round a bent wing on the Gedge. It is important that the sharp edge continues right round these shapes. There are no nickers, so the cutting edge forms the outside of the cut. Make sure that this cutting edge is at the maximum diameter of the tool – it is very easy to diminish the tool's diameter when forming the clearance bevel. The screw is identical to that described for the Jennings and Irwin bits.

Expansive Bits

There are two separate parts to an expansive bit. The centre part comprises the screw, the top thread of which is extended to form a cutter. The detachable blade has a nicker at its outermost end and a cutter along its bottom edge. The nicker is sharpened on the inside only, using a three-cornered file. The cutting edge is filed on the underside to a clearance angle. The top surface is curved, and is honed with a curved slip stone. The cutter part of the screw is filed on the inside with a small, flat, needle file. There is no spare metal on the expansive bit, so any sharpening should be kept to a minimum.

Forstner and Saw-toothed Bits

The Forstner and saw-toothed bits are very similar. Apart from the teeth filed in the skirt of the latter, the sharpening is identical. They are not easy to sharpen. Getting at the bevel that runs round the inside of the skirt is difficult, as movement of a file or stone in this area is restricted. The file has to be drawn around the bevel – it cannot be used in a push-stroke fashion, as is customary. There is no spare metal in the skirt, so the minimum of metal is removed. The skirt positions the bit when it is in use, the centre point only being there to facilitate the initial positioning of the tool. It thus protrudes only slightly in front of the skirt. The cutter is sharpened from above by using a flat file in the slot through which the waste escapes. Under no circumstances remove metal from the outside circumference of the tool. The teeth seldom need to be sharpened. If they need reshaping, a tapered saw file is the ideal tool to use.

Machine Auger Bits

The speed at which a bit is turned by machine is much higher than when it is being used by hand. If the bit has a screw it is pulled into the wood at an uncontrollable speed, so the screw is usually replaced by a point that has no thread. The cutters and nickers are similar to those found on the Irwin and Jennings bits. Apart from the point, the bit is sharpened in exactly the same way. The point needs occasional sharpening with a file. Make sure that the tip of the point is in the centre of the cutting circle, or starting the bit will become very difficult.

Parrot-nose Bit

This tool has numerous names, bobbin and scillop being just two often used. The modern application of this tool is in the long auger form used for boring the hole in lamp standards. The basic tool looks similar to the shell bit except for the cutting end. This is formed by grinding half the nose away and bending the part left back to form a cutting edge. There is very little scope for sharpening, though it is possible to make a few strokes on the underside of the cutter with a fine stone. The cutter is extremely thin, and if the bevel is sharpened it rapidly disappears.

Twist Drills

Two different twist drills are used by woodworkers: the standard twist drill made from high carbon, or high-speed steel, and the dowel drill with a centre point. Both types have to be ground as they are very hard. The twist drill as bought from the toolshop is usually ground with angles suitable for drilling metal, though they work well for most woodworking purposes. The angles shown in Fig 13.4 should be

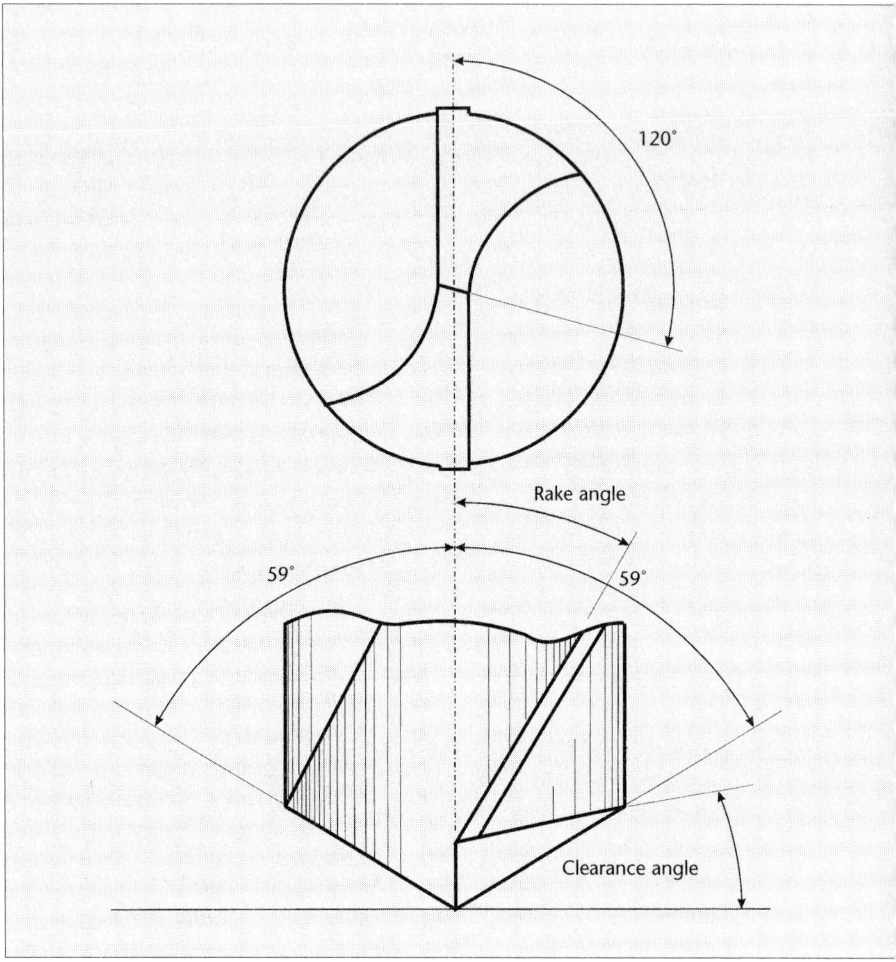

Fig 13.4 Sharpening angles for twist drills.

maintained when regrinding. This is best achieved by using an attachment for an electric drill, or a jig on the grinding machine. The dowel drill with its centre point is best treated by hand. The tools used depend on the material from which the drill is made. Some are soft enough to file, but others require a stone, and a diamond-coated file is ideal for this purpose. The dowel drill has spurs and cutters similar to an auger bit. The cutters are sharpened from the underside, while the spurs can only be sharpened from the inside.

CHAPTER 14

Machine Tool Cutters

Balance

Nearly all woodcutting machines perform their task with a rotating cutting action. This involves two things not met with when preparing hand tools for use. Instead of making a continuous cut, the work is accomplished by removing a series of chips, and the only hand tool used in this way is the adze. Machine cutters revolve at very high speeds, so the balance of cutters revolving at these speeds is most important as all forces acting on a revolving block must be balanced by an equal and opposite force. This means that even the smallest imbalance will load the machine bearings in a way they were not designed to resist. If all the cutters in a block are the same size and weight, and set to the same projection, the block is said to be in **static balance**, though this does not necessarily mean that the block and cutters will be in balance when running at high speed (**dynamic balance**).

It is a basic law of motion that once a body is in motion it will continue to move in a straight line and will resist any effort to change its travelling direction. **Centripetal force** is thus present in the caps and bolts stopping the cutters from flying out of the revolving block. The force exerted by the cutter trying to fly out of the block in a straight line is **centrifugal**. This must be resisted by an equal and opposite force (centripetal) in the caps and bolts. Imbalance affects the quality of the work being produced, and also places undue strain on the spindle and bearings of the machine. Severely out of balance cutters may eventually fly out of the revolving block. A spindle moulder cutter travelling across the workshop at 120mph is a lethal projectile.

All the cutting edges in a block must be set so that they all cut exactly the same path. This is so they all do an equal amount of work and give the best possible finish to the cut surface. This applies equally to solid cutters, even those used in electric routers. Cutters working at this speed generate heat, and are kept cool by dissipating the heat into the timber being cut. It is therefore important to adhere to the correct feed speed. Blunt cutters generate far more heat than cutters in good condition. Cutters that leave a scorched surface on the finished material are in a poor condition, or the feed speed is incorrect.

Planing Machine Cutters

Planing machines, both over- and underhand, have blocks with two, three or four cutters. The cutters must be kept in sets, which helps to preserve the balance of the set. When grinding, try to remove the same amount of metal from each blade. It is helpful if the cutters can be accurately weighed so that all the cutters in a set can be kept in static balance. It is impossible to grind the cutters freehand, so some form of attachment for the grinding machine is necessary. Professional mills have special machines for this purpose.

Cutters (referred to in the trade as knives) can be made from several different materials: high carbon steel, high-speed steel, and tungsten-

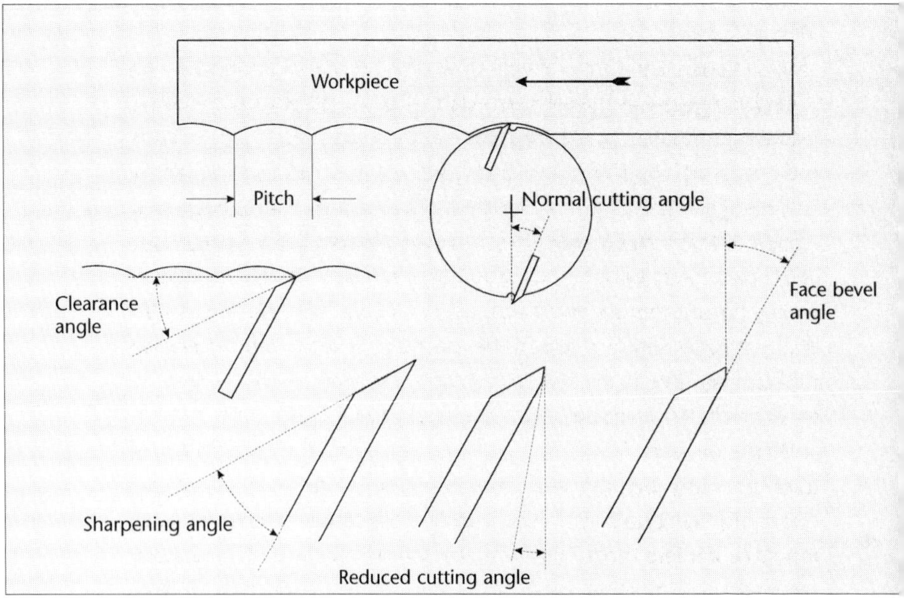

Fig 14.1 Sharpening angles for planing machine cutters.

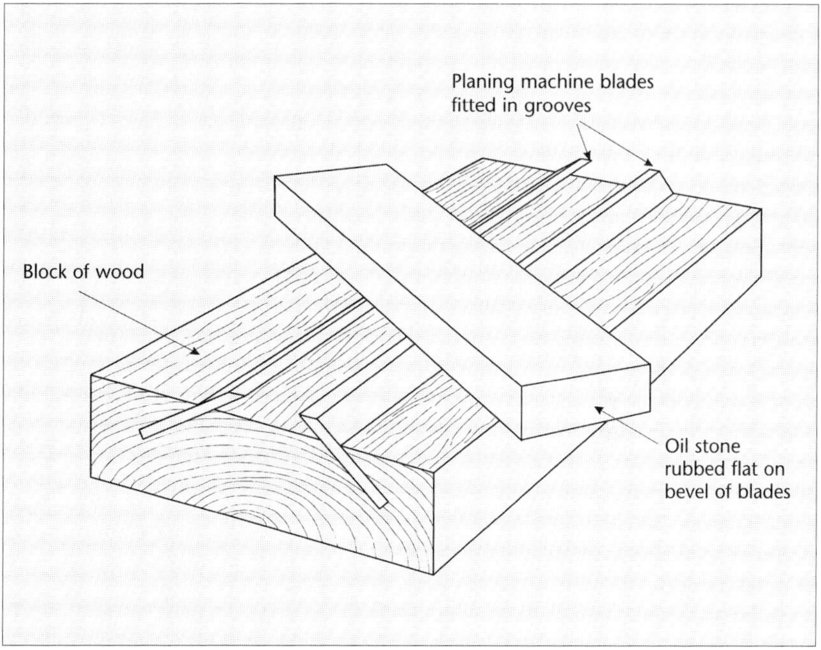

Fig 14.2 Honing planing machine blades.

carbide tipped. Each of these materials requires a different composition grinding wheel (see Chapter 4). Most cutters have a single bevel, usually 30°. When grinding, three things must be maintained: straightness of edge, angle of bevel and balance. Occasionally a face angle is put on the knives (Fig 14.1). This makes the cutting edge stouter so that it can withstand more rigorous use on very hard timber. Once the cutters have been ground they are honed, which is carried out by honing them in pairs mounted in a block of wood (Fig 14.2). This is done occasionally to revive a dull edge, but this is a stop-gap measure and should not be carried out too often as there is no way of ensuring the resultant cutting path of the knife.

Take care when installing the cutters. Not only must all the knives track properly, but there is a personal safety factor to consider. Changing the cutters should always be done when there is plenty of time to complete the operation – never leave the job until you have completed it. The machine should be electrically isolated and locked off, and the type of isolating lock that can have a padlock passed

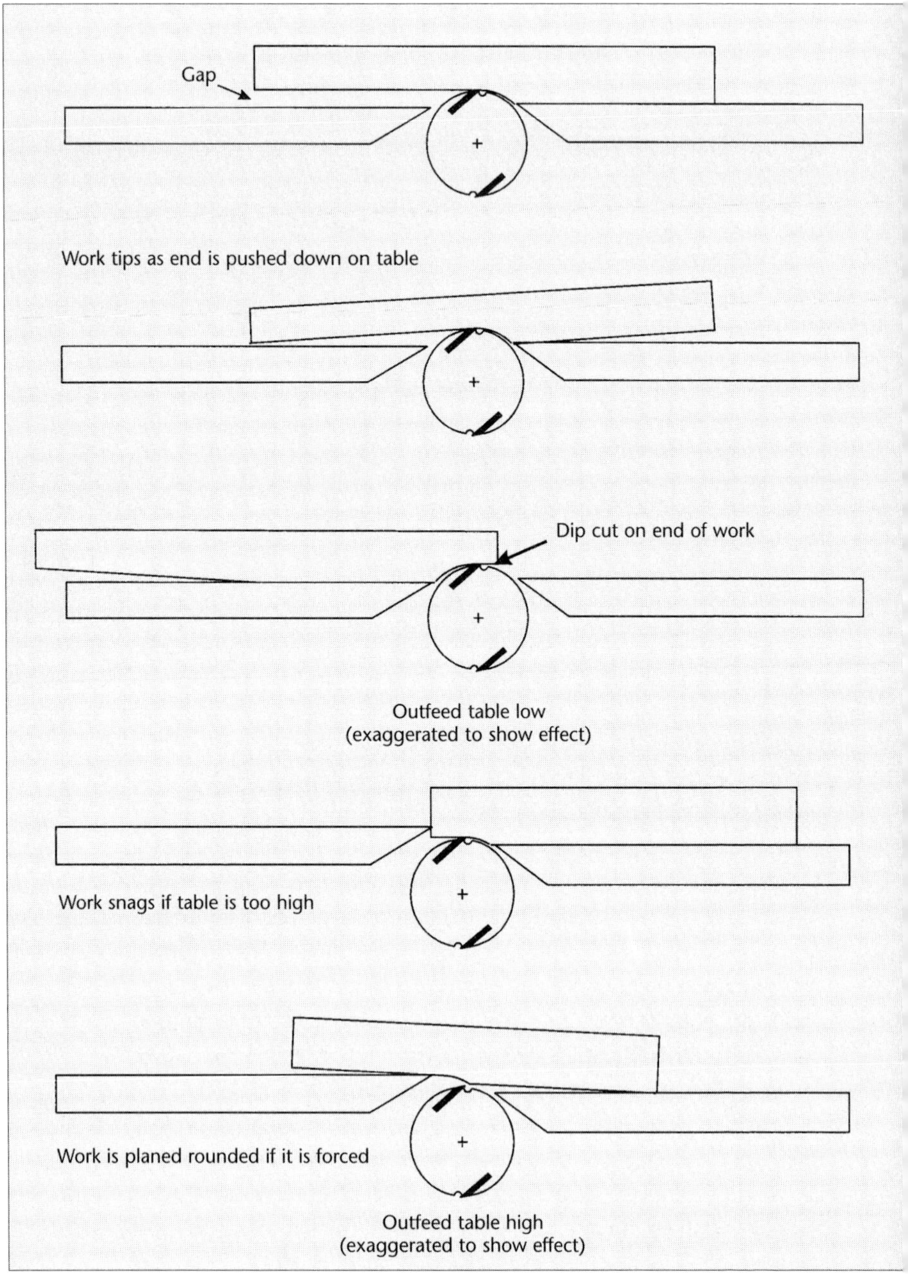

Fig 14.3 The effects of setting the outfeed table incorrectly.

through it is recommended. The amount the cutters project is determined by the outfeed table (Fig 14.3). Setting the projection accurately is accomplished as shown in Fig 14.4.

Spindle Moulder Cutters

The spindle moulder (called a 'shaper' in the USA) is probably the most ubiquitous woodworking machine, and it is therefore not surprising that there are so many different types of cutters, blocks and attachments for it. Four different types of blocks (sometimes called 'heads') are shown in Fig 14.5. The solid-profile block is used where thousands of metres of the same section have to be produced,

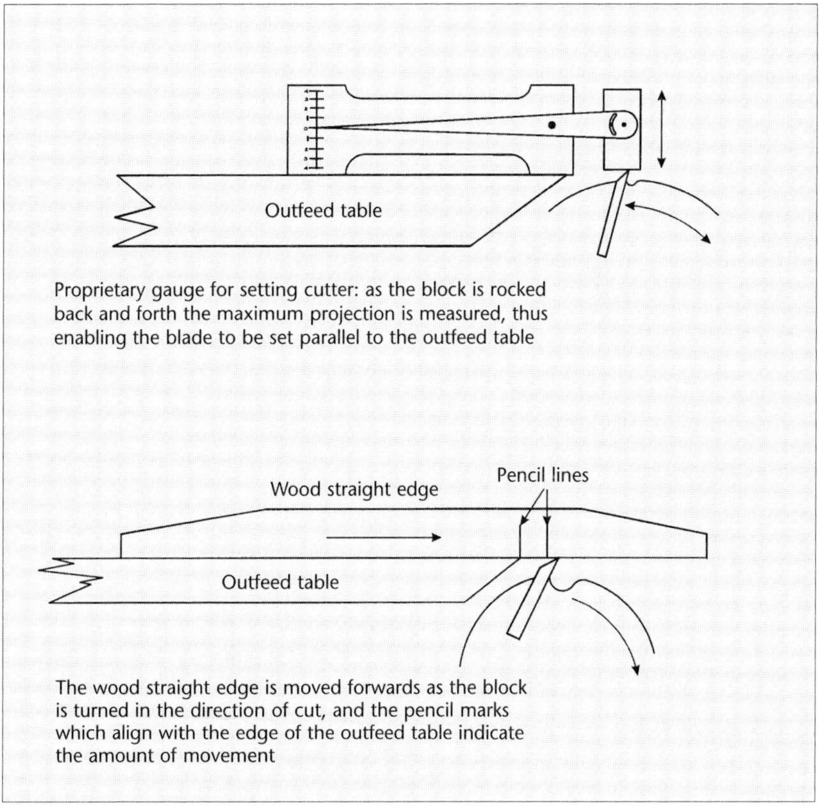

Fig 14.4 Methods of setting the cutter correctly.

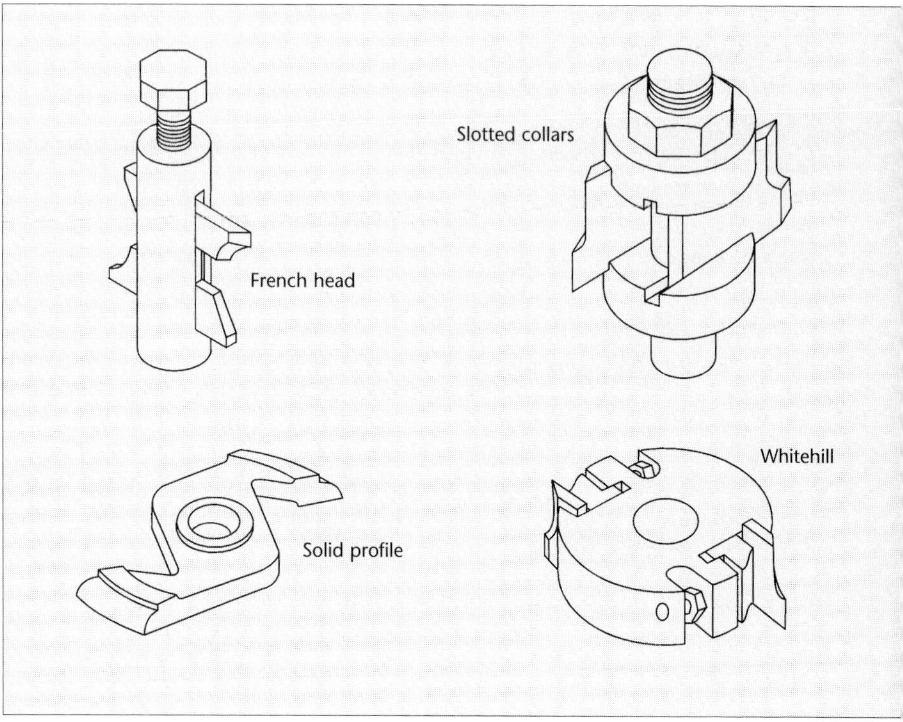

Fig 14.5 Spindle moulder cutter blocks.

and the cutting face is usually made from tungsten carbide. Special-profile grinders are used to service this cutter, and most solid heads are sent to a specialist for refurbishment. The only in-house treatment might be an occasional stoning of the flat face with a diamond plate.

Cutters for all types of head, except for the French head, need some geometry to establish their true shape (it is only French head cutters that are a true reversal of the work's contour). Much of what I have said above concerning the bevels on planer knives applies to spindle moulder cutters, though the profiled cutting edge requires shaped grinding wheels to form the edge. Some blank cutting blades are soft enough to file to shape. However the bevel is formed it should be finished with a stone. The setting of the blades in the block is important, as both tracking and balance must be maintained. Some workshops have a dummy spindle on which the head is mounted for setting up. This is equipped with devices to ensure exact setting of the cutters.

French head cutters are the easiest to produce. The action of the cutters in a French head is different from those in all other heads: because the cutting edge is in line with the centre of the spindle it has a scraping action as opposed to the cutting action of other heads. The metal from which French head cutters are made is relatively soft compared with that of other cutters, and can be easily filed to shape. Once the bevel (usually 30°) has been formed and honed, the flat face is rubbed on a stone to remove any burr. A ticketer is used to turn the edge similar to that of a cabinet scraper. This gives the cutting edge some lead. French heads are not very efficient, but setting up is quick and easy, and they are therefore used for short run work.

Router Cutters

Unless you have special profile grinding equipment, only the inside flat face of the cutter should be stoned. Router cutters are made from different materials: carbon steel, high-speed steel, tungsten-carbide

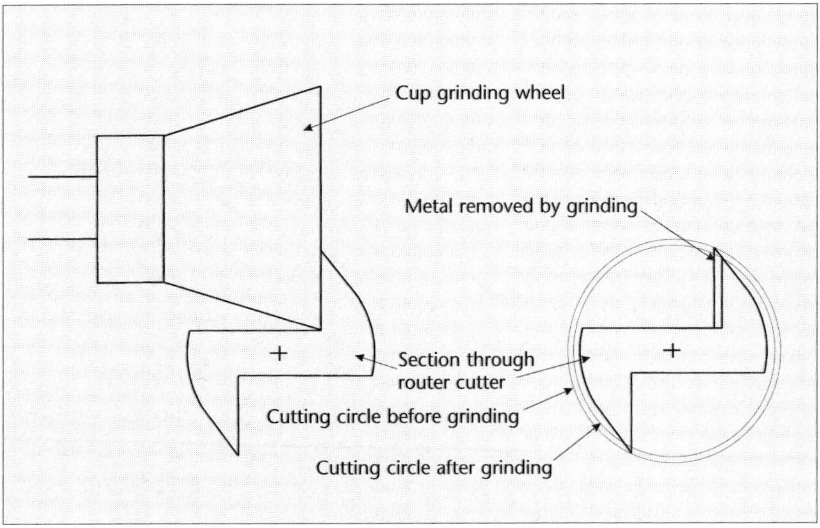

Fig 14.6 Grinding reduces the effective cutting diameter of router cutters.

tipped, solid tungsten and diamond bonded. For all these, except for diamond bonded, a small diamond slip made by DMT is the ideal tool. Only sharpen the flat face. Never attempt to sharpen the bevel or clearance angle. Apart from the cheap carbon and high-speed cutters, restoration should be carried out by a specialist firm equipped with the proper expensive machinery. Attachments, supplied with full operating instructions, are available to fit on to the

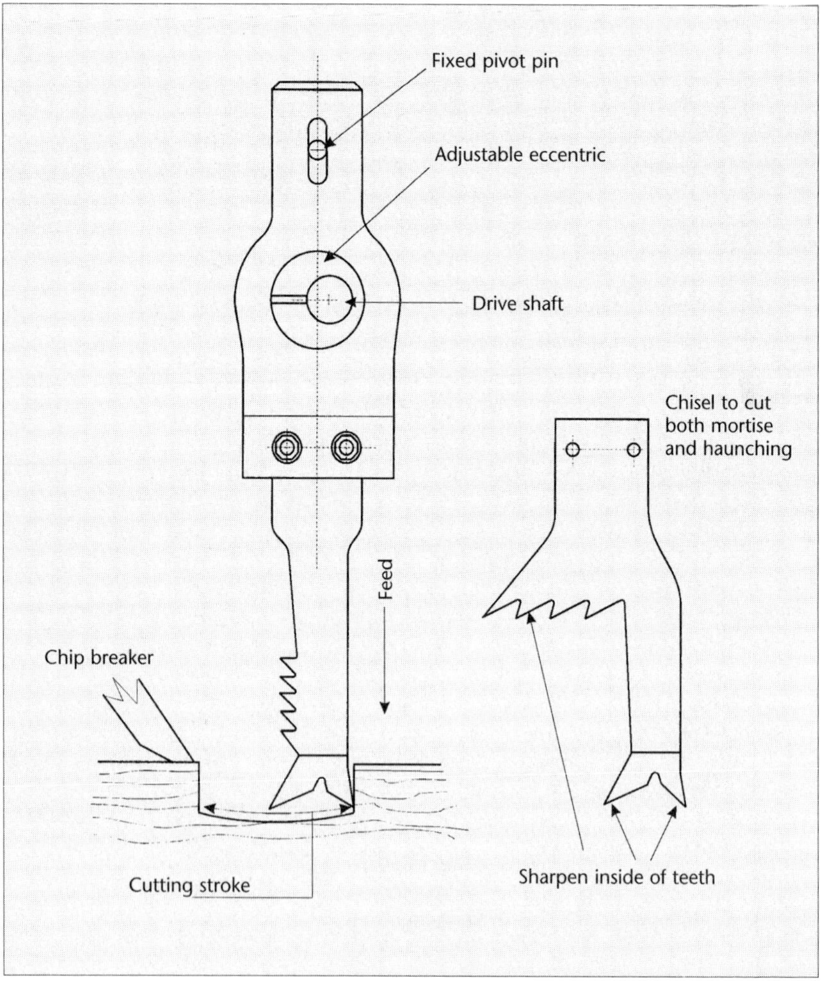

Fig 14.7 The principles of the Maka mortising system.

base of the router for grinding straight-fluted cutters. As they remove metal from the inside flat face of the cutter, however, the cutting diameter of the tool is reduced (Fig 14.6).

Mortising Cutters

There are several ways of cutting a mortise by machine. The Maka system (Fig 14.7) chisels are sharpened with a stone on the inside faces of the teeth. On no account should metal be removed from the

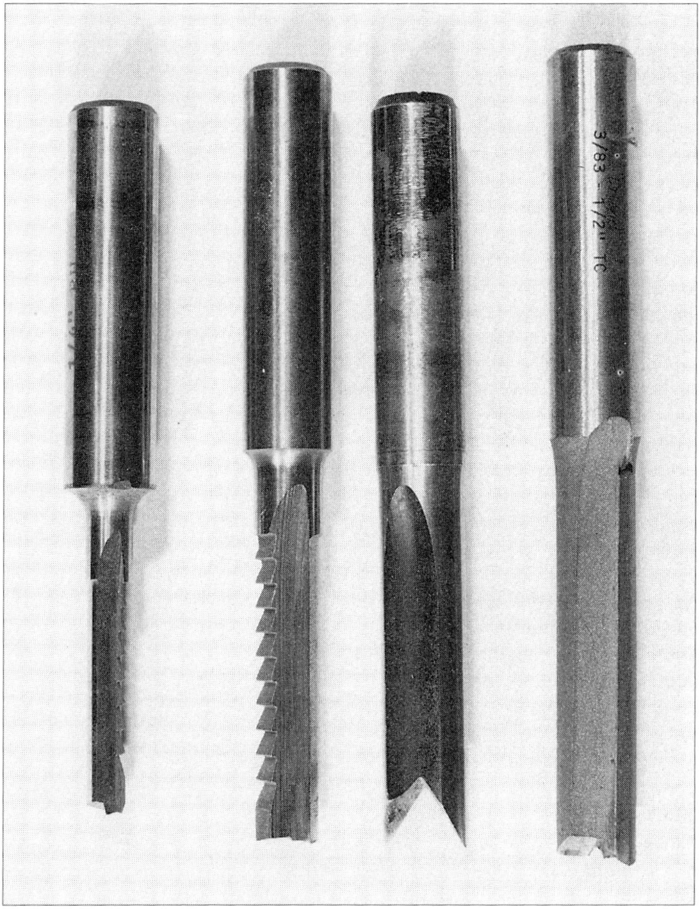

Fig 14.8 Slot mortising cutters.

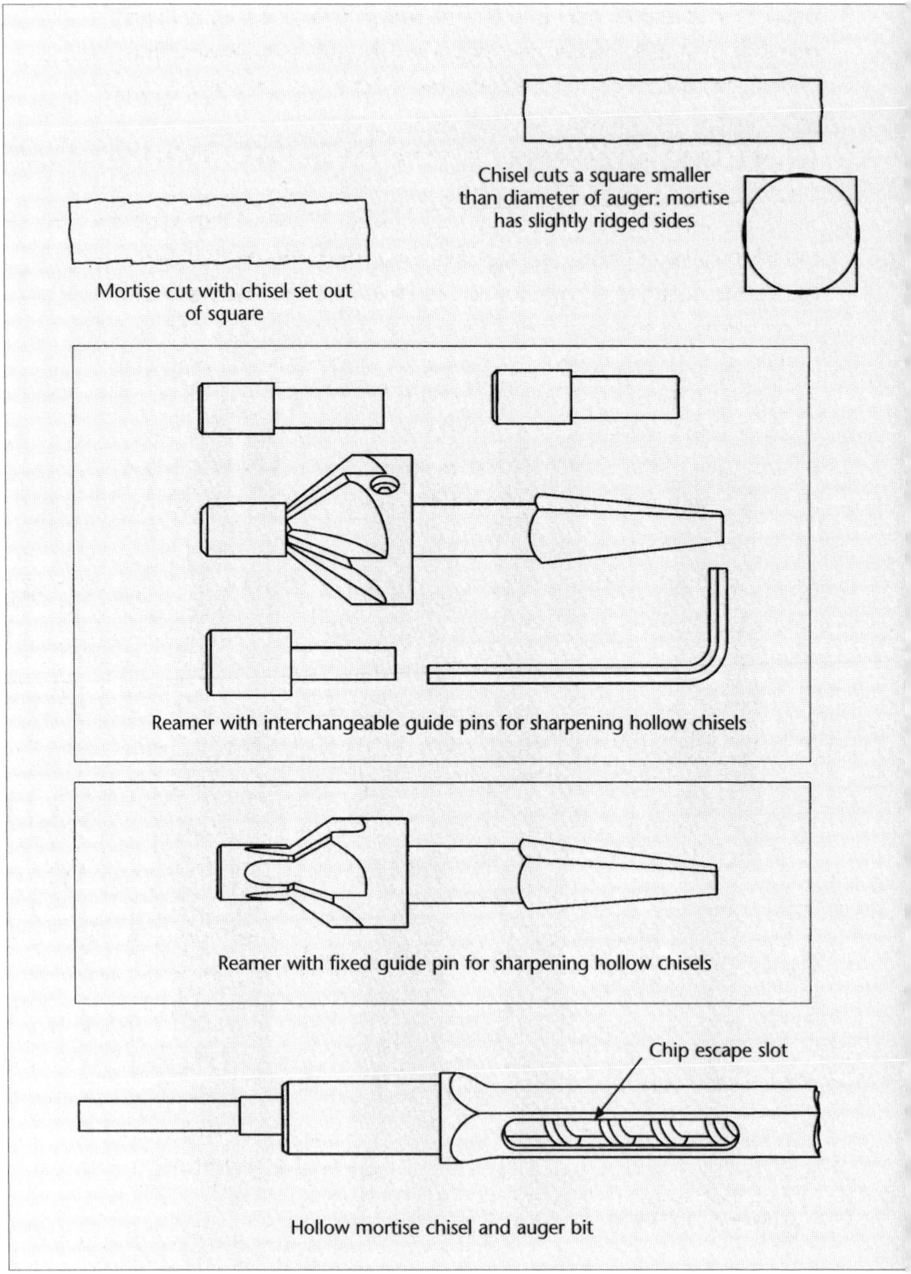

Fig 14.9 Hollow chisel details.

outside faces as this would reduce the tool's clearance. Sharpening details are in the handbook supplied with these machines. The chisels are made from high-speed steel. The angles of the cutting faces are critical and must be maintained.

The oscillating bit mortising machine is also known as a slotter or jigger, and two designs of bit are used on it (Fig 14.8). The teeth on the improved design masticate the waste and aid its removal from the mortise, but both designs rely on the cutting faces at the tip of the tool doing most of the work. These faces can be sharpened with a slip stone, being careful to maintain the original angles. As the cutters revolve at high speed they tend to collect a deposit of resin from soft wood, which is best removed with a brush and paraffin (kerosene).

The hollow chisel mortiser requires the sharpening of two separate items. The chisel is sharpened on the inside with the reamer (Fig 14.9), and the outside face of the chisel should be rubbed flat

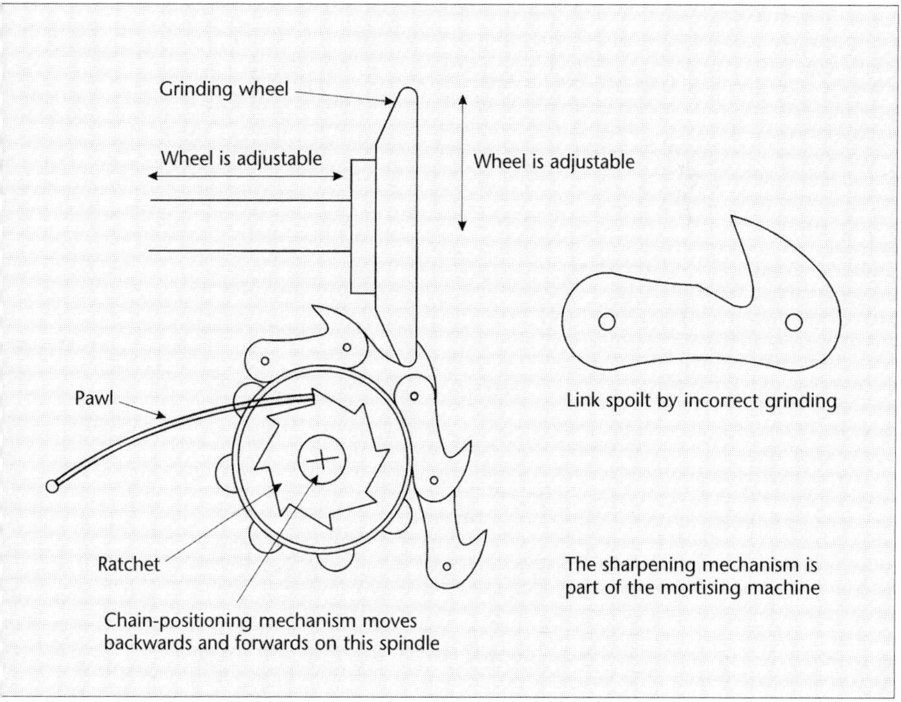

Fig 14.10 Sharpening a mortising chain.

on a fine stone after the reaming has been completed. The auger bit requires sharpening similarly to the description given for auger bits in Chapter 13 (Fig 13.3).

Chain mortising machines usually have an attachment for grinding the chain, which comprises a bevelled grinding wheel that can be adjusted to alter its angle and grinding height. The chain is supported on a sprocket that slides under the grinding wheel, the sprocket being indexed so that each link is accurately presented to the wheel. It is important that the correct link shape is maintained (Fig 14.10). The face of the links may be honed with a slip stone. After grinding, all abrasive and grinding particles must be removed from the chain before it is lubricated and reinstalled.

Alternax chisels can be ground and honed in similar style to a hand mortise chisel (see Chapter 9). The bevels must be maintained to give clearance to the swinging chisel (Fig 14.11).

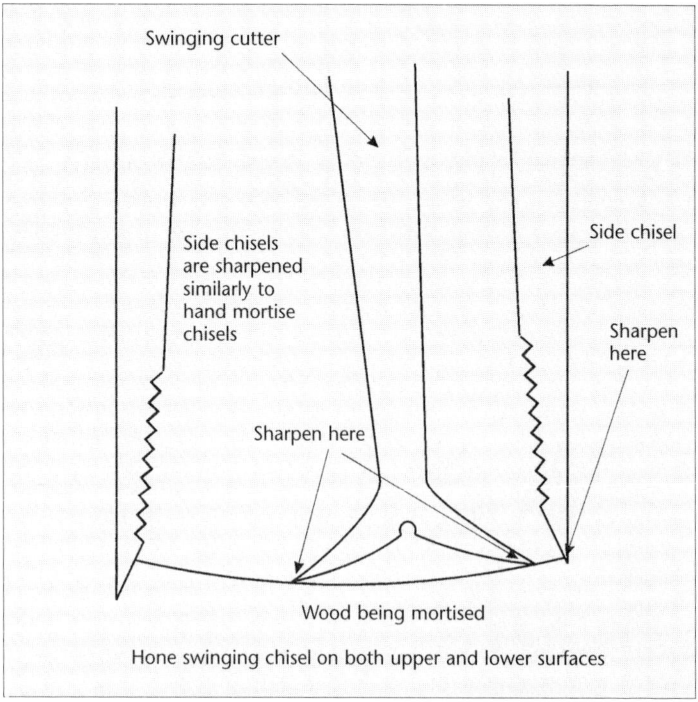

Fig 14.11 Alternax mortising machine chisels.

CHAPTER 15

Machine Saw Blades

Machines used for sawing wood can be divided into two groups. The circular saw is a circular plate with teeth around its periphery, while the band saw is a continuous loop of steel with teeth formed on one edge. Both types of machine are made in a wide range of sizes. The circular saw's size is specified by the diameter of the blade. Band saw machines are described by the diameter of the wheels over which the blade passes. Both machines are made in basic to very complex versions. Hand-fed circular saws up to and including 12in (305mm) are dealt with here, though books are listed in the bibliography which deal with large machines should you require that information. Band saw machines with blades over 3in (76mm) need special treatment, and their blades are always serviced by a saw doctor.

Circular Saws

There is an optimum speed for the periphery of a circular saw blade. The spindle on most machines revolves at only one speed, which means that the size of the blade is determined by the spindle speed. The recommended periphery speed for the saw blade is 10,000ft/min (3,000m/min) in round figures – about 112 miles (180km) per hour. Teeth passing the wood at this speed generate heat, which is dissipated into the timber. Blunt teeth generate far more heat than sharp teeth and they cut slower. The blade heats up and the periphery becomes hot, though the centre of the blade away from the cutting edge remains cool. Any heat here is conducted away by the spindle into the bulk of the machine. As metal expands with heat, the periphery of the saw expands, but the centre stops it taking on a larger circumference. The cutting edge thus has to become wavy to accommodate the expansion, and the saw will no longer cut in a straight line. As the saw cut becomes crooked the sides of the kerf bind on the saw blade, causing more friction and consequently more heat. The blade jams in the wood,

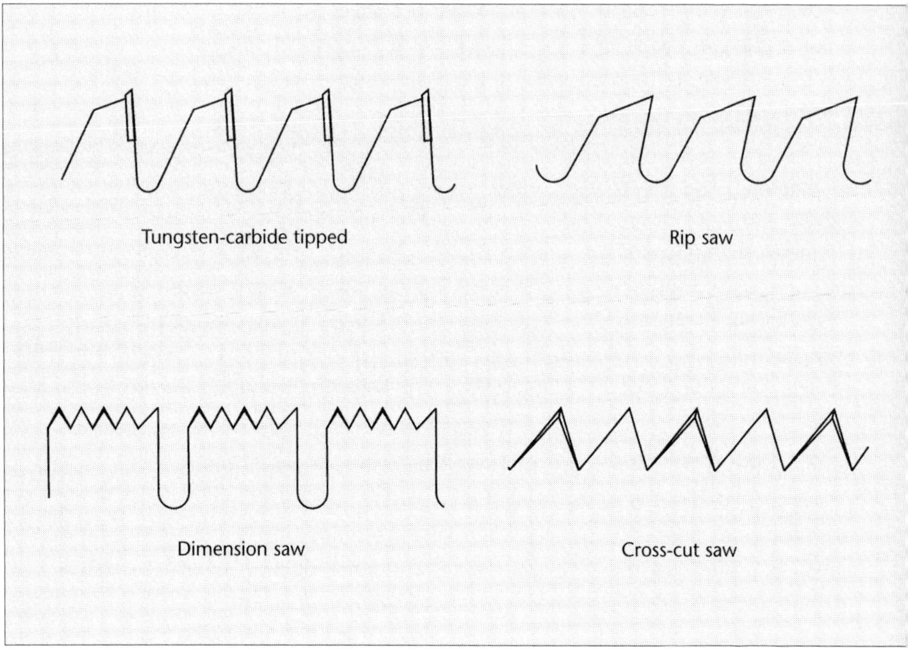

Fig 15.1 Circular saw tooth shapes.

which is picked up by the back of the blade, and an accident can occur. The edge of the saw blade needs to be rigid to cut straight, and although centrifugal force contributes in some way to this requirement, it is insufficient. The saw blade (known as a 'plate') is tensioned, a task that requires skill and knowledge. It is carried out by a saw doctor beating the plate on a crowned anvil with a dog-head hammer. A saw plate reduces in diameter as it is sharpened, and after a number of sharpenings it has to be re-tensioned. Larger saws need more care and more frequent tensioning than smaller ones.

Tooth Configuration

Circular saw teeth vary in much the same way as those of hand saws (Chapter 12). The cutting edges of the teeth used for ripping have chisel edges and a positive rake, while cross-cutting teeth have pointed tips and a negative rake (Fig 15.1). There is a third type of tooth used on cut-off saws, which are designed to cut at an angle to the grain. The cut-off saw is sometimes referred to as a 'multi-purpose' saw (which it is not) or a 'novelty' saw.

Saws with large teeth are referred to as coarse, while those with small teeth are called fine. Special saws are made for cutting sheet material such as plywood and laminates. A fine saw is needed for this purpose to prevent the lower face from breaking out or becoming whiskered. These saws often have extreme negative rake.

Saws with tungsten-carbide tipped (TCT) teeth require special sharpening equipment, and most toolshops act as agents for a saw doctor who will refurbish these tools. The saw plate that carries the tipped teeth has slots cut around its circumference to take care of edge expansion. For the small workshop TCT blades are a sound investment; they are never as sharp as a properly maintained steel blade but remain in a usable condition for very much longer.

Saw Filing

Three things are necessary for saw plate maintenance. The teeth must be in a true working circle, that is to say, the tip of every tooth on the plate must describe the same circle. The teeth must be set so

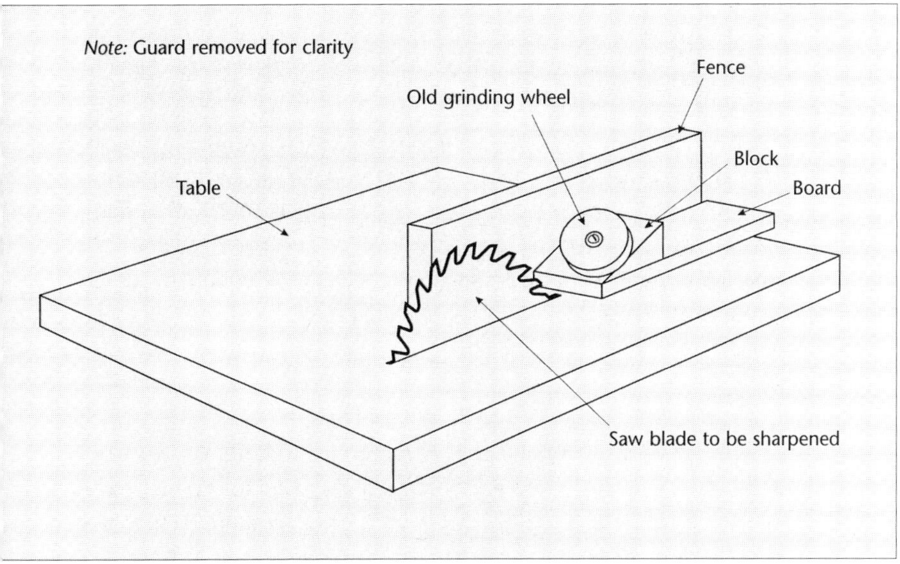

Fig 15.2 Stoning a circular saw.

that the plate has clearance in the kerf. Sharpness must be maintained.

Because a small clearance is needed between the hole in the centre of the plate and the spindle it is important that the saw is always put on the spindle in the same orientation. If the machine has a drive pin, the spindle is turned until the pin is at top dead centre. If there is no drive pin the blade is always put on the spindle so the maker's name is at the top. To ensure that the teeth are all working in a true circle the blade is 'stoned' with a workshop-made

Fig 15.3 Device for setting circular saw teeth.

Fig 15.4 Saw plate installed on the device shown in Fig 15.3.

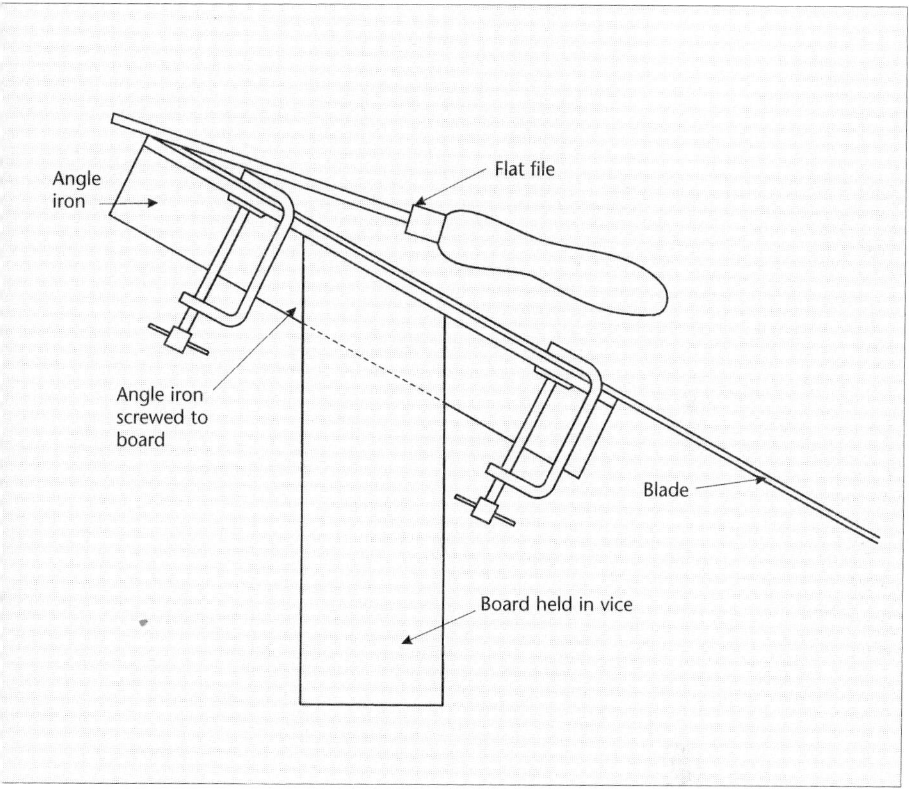

Fig 15.5 Filing a lap bevel on a band saw blade.

device (Fig 15.2). The grindstone is gently presented to the saw while it is running, which tops each tooth and gives a reference point when filing.

It is essential to hold the plate firmly when it is being filed. The best way of doing this is to mount it between two flat boards with ends shaped to a slightly smaller circumference than the saw blade. A bolt passes through each of the boards and the hole in the centre of the plate. This assembly can be held vertically in a vice at a convenient height for filing. For most saws a mill file is used. This is a single-cut flat file with rounded edges. When filing, the flat top on the tooth produced during stoning is just removed. The depth of gullet must be maintained. Every fourth or fifth sharpening, scribe a line on the side of the plate with a pair of dividers. The gullets are

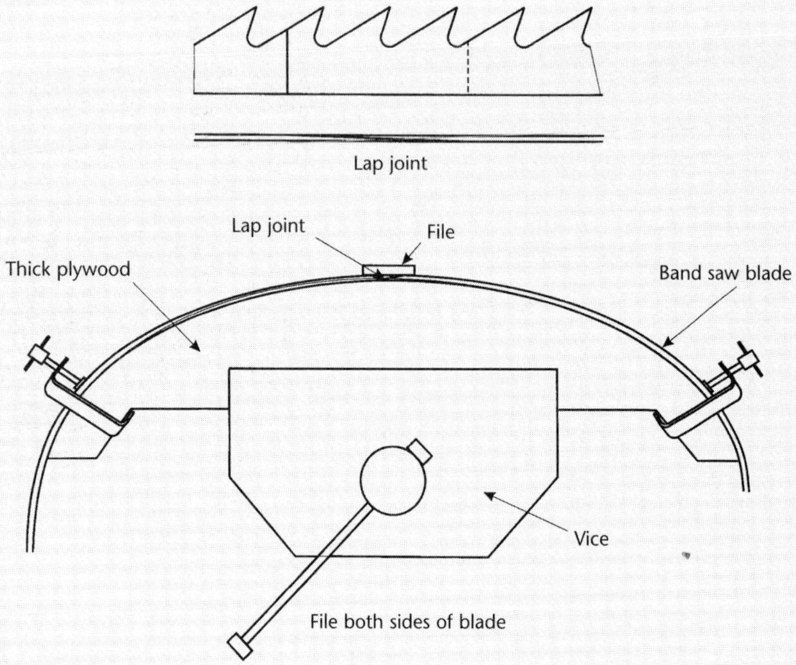

Fig 15.6 Jig for filing the sides of a band saw after brazing.

filed down to this line with the edge of the mill file. Triangular teeth are filed with a three-cornered saw file in exactly the same way as hand saw teeth are filed (Chapter 12).

The teeth on circular saws are set by bending them. This needs to be done accurately. The device shown in Figs 15.3 and 15.4 is the normal appliance used in small workshops.

Band Saw Blades

It is not economic to sharpen band saw blades under ¾in (19mm) wide. Most narrow band saw blades made today have hardened teeth which are difficult to sharpen or set. Buy the blade in bulk lengths, usually sold in 100ft or 30m coils. Joining the blade is not difficult. The lapped joint and methods of filing it are shown in Figs 15.5 and 15.6. Brazing is easiest done with an electric machine (Fig 15.7), though it is possible to do this with a simple workshop-made jig and a propane or butane blowlamp. The surfaces to be brazed must be clean and coated with flux. Brazing metal is sold in a thin strip. Cut a piece off and place it between the two faces to be brazed. Heat the joint until the brazing metal becomes a liquid. Grip the joint tight with a pair of pliers, forcing the two parts into close contact. Re-heat the joint to

Fig 15.7 Machine for electrically brazing band saw blades.

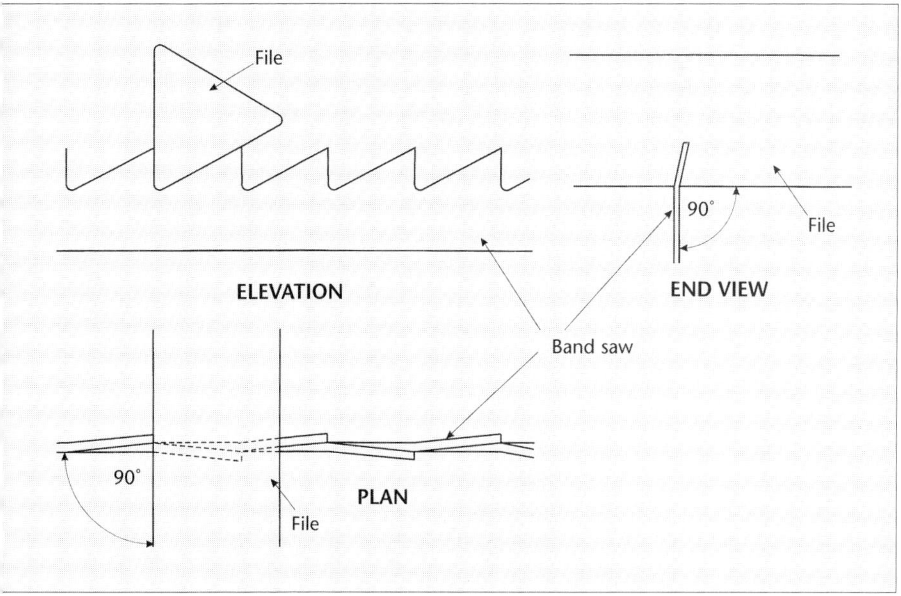

Fig 15.8 Sharpening a band saw blade.

a dull cherry red and then allow it to cool slowly. This is to ensure that the blade in the area of the join is not brittle. If this last procedure is not carried out the blade will fracture close to the join, particularly common on machines with small wheels.

Filing and Setting Blades

Not all band saw blades have teeth that are of a shape suitable for filing by hand. They are normally sharpened on a machine that uses a small grinding wheel. If the teeth are the type that can be filed then the blade is held in a saw-sharpening block or chops (Chapter 12). Using a tapered saw file, proceed very similarly to sharpening a hand rip saw; Fig 15.8 shows the rake and tooth configuration. Setting can be accomplished with a pliers saw set. There is a special version made for band saws (Fig 15.9), but for most narrow blades any pliers set will do. Band saw blades when not on the machine should be folded. This makes them easy to store, but more importantly it makes them much safer to handle. You may find it difficult to fold the blade the first few times, but it soon becomes second nature. Follow the step-by-step illustrations in Figs 15.10–15.17.

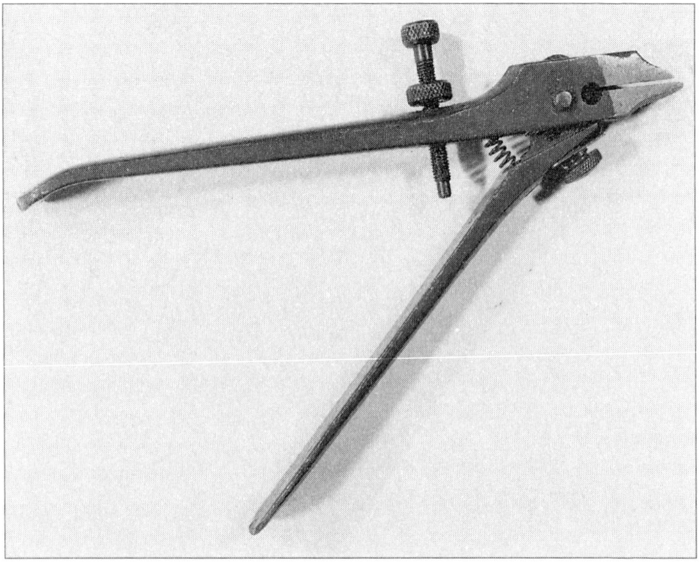

Fig 15.9 Tool for setting band saw teeth.

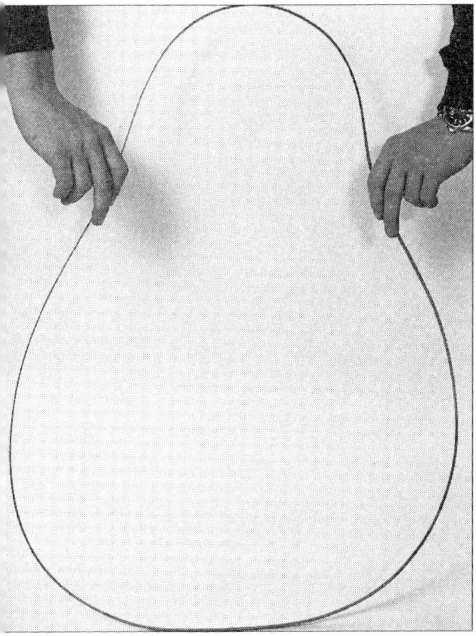

ig 15.10 Hold the band saw as shown, with our thumbs on the outside of the blade and ointing towards you.

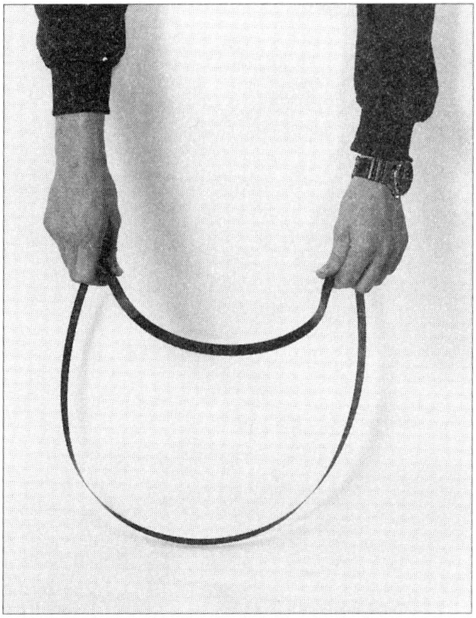

Fig 15.11 Twist your thumbs towards one another. This will force the top of the blade away from you.

g 15.12 Continue forcing the top downwards.

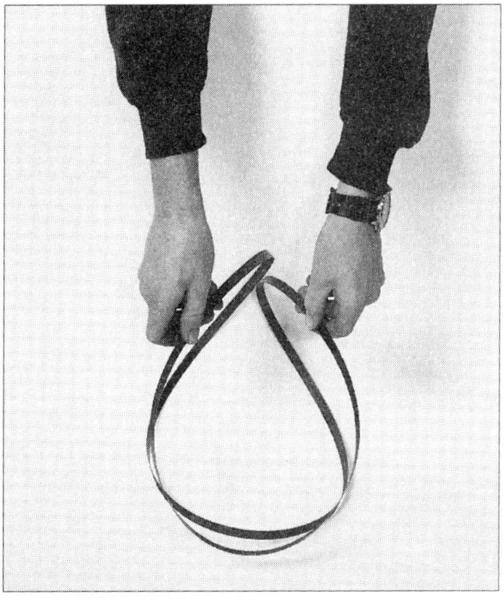

Fig 15.13 Allow the bottom loop to lie on the floor.

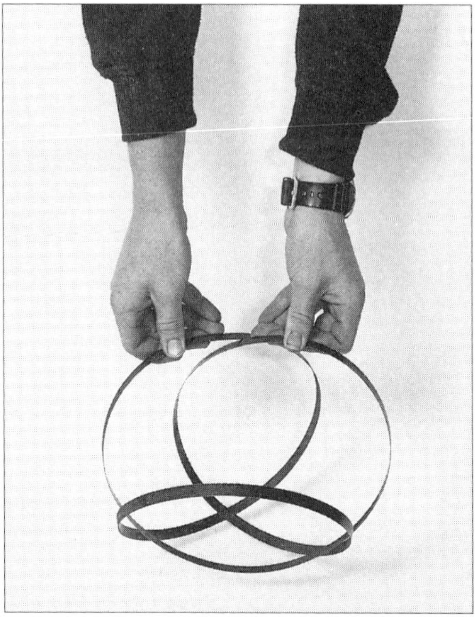

Fig 15.14 Tip the top loop into the bottom loop and bring the hands together.

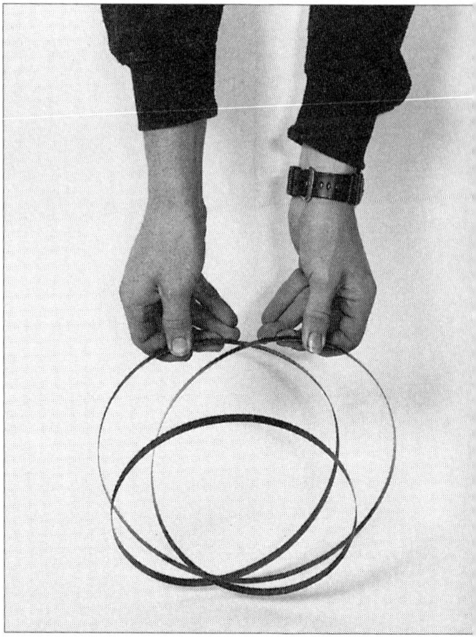

Fig 15.15 Keep the loops pushed down on the floor.

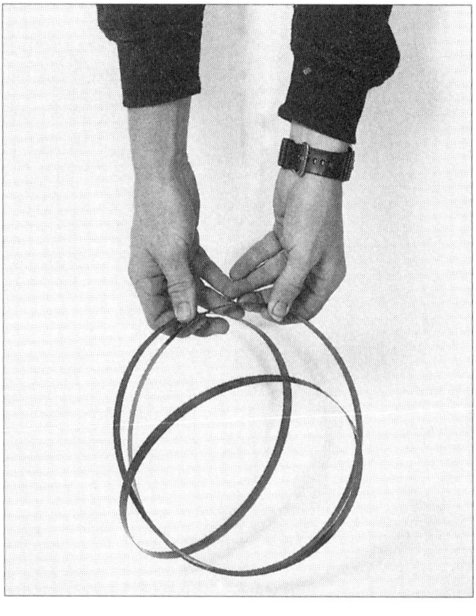

Fig 15.16 The blade will spring into three loops.

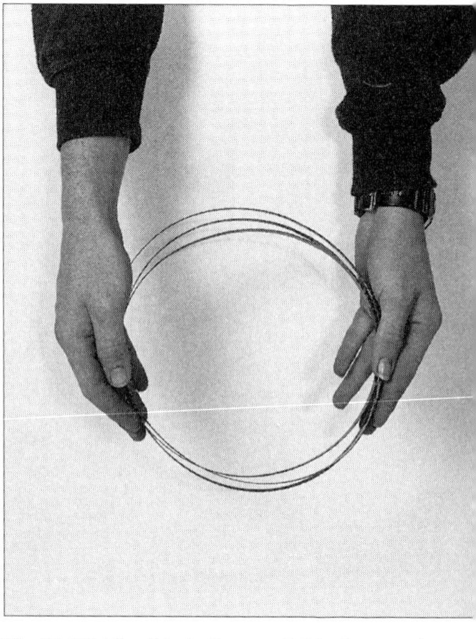

Fig 15.17 The blade is now folded up and can easily be stored.

CHAPTER 16

Scrapers

Cabinet Scrapers

The cabinet scraper is the most uncomplicated tool in the woodworker's tool chest, though it is not a simple tool to sharpen. The nature of the steel from which the scraper is made is very important. The steel not only has to hold a sharp edge, it also has to be malleable enough to form the hook, and many pieces of steel sold as scrapers do not fill this requirement. Scrapers cut from the worn-out blade of an old hand saw are usually ideal. The edge of a cabinet scraper is quite different from the cutting edge on any other tool (Fig 16.1). Sharpening this tool is quite straightforward, but most people have difficulty obtaining a good cutting edge. The tool should remove a fine, thin shaving. If it just makes dust, it is not sharp.

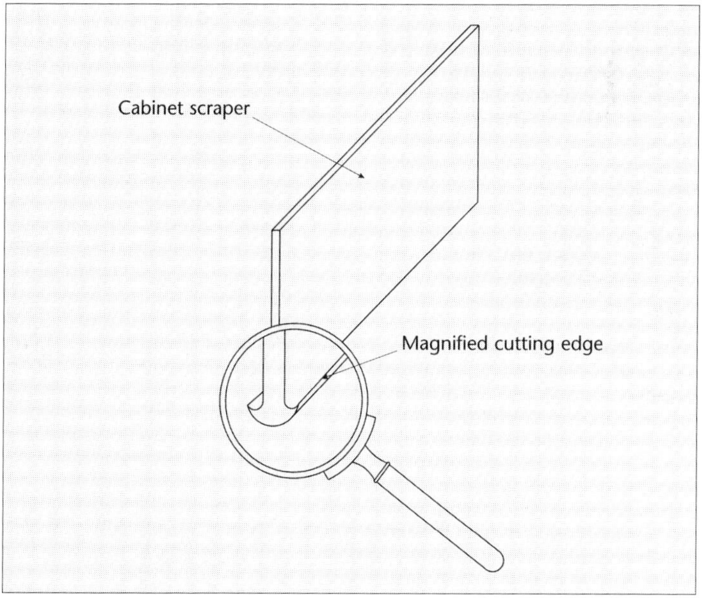

Fig 16.1 Cutting edge of a cabinet scraper.

The faces of the steel must be flat and smooth – steel with rust pitting is unsuitable. Any marks left by surface grinding must be polished away on a fine hone. The scraper is placed in a vice with the edge to be sharpened uppermost. The edge is draw filed to make it straight and square, and file marks are removed by rubbing the edge on an oil stone. The edge must be kept at 90° to the sides. The next part of the process requires a tool made of hard steel, called a 'ticketer'. Some tools used for other purposes can be used, – a nail punch or a small gouge will do. I make my ticketers by grinding all the teeth off a small three-cornered file, and then polishing its surfaces on a fine stone. The surface of the ticketer must be smooth. The higher the surface finish the better.

Hold the scraper in a piece of rag to protect the hands, as the corners of the steel are sharp. Put the end of the scraper against the bench. Holding the scraper firmly, draw the ticketer along the corner of the steel (Fig 16.2). Three or four passes are required, increasing the angle between the ticketer and the scraper each time. The pressure applied between the ticketer and the steel should be firm but not excessive. The hook formed on the corner of the scraper does not need

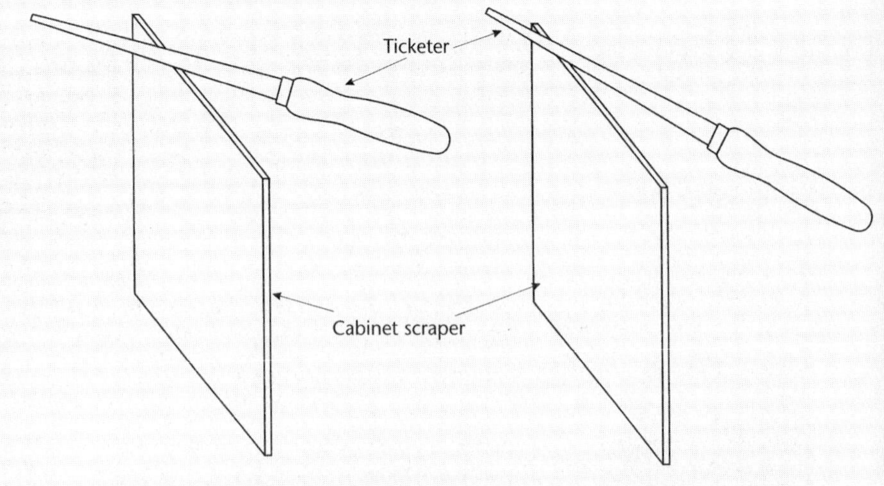

The ticketer is drawn along the corner of the scraper several times with moderate pressure, the angle of the ticketer being increased each time

Fig 16.2 Sharpening a cabinet scraper.

to be large – trying to form a large hook tends to lead to a blunt scraper.

There is a tool made to form the hook on the scraper (Fig 16.3) which requires little skill to use. The tool comprises a block of wood with a piece of metal angle on its underside. A hardened steel wheel with a rounded edge protrudes through the metal angle. The scraper has the edge prepared in exactly the same way as when using the ticketer. It is held in the vice so that the sharpening tool can run along the edge to be sharpened. It requires only one pass with moderate pressure on the tool to produce a usable hook.

Two edges of the scraper can be sharpened, which gives four cutting edges. In use the edge does not last long. Resharpening does not always require the edge filing process. It is possible to place the scraper flat on the bench and to burnish the face flat so that the hook is turned back flat. A new hook is then formed in the normal way.

Scraper Planes

The cabinet scraper has two failings: it is hard on the hands in use, and it easily works hollows in the face of the work being scraped. The use of a scraper plane overcomes these faults. The blade is

Fig 16.3 A tool for forming the hook on cabinet scrapers.

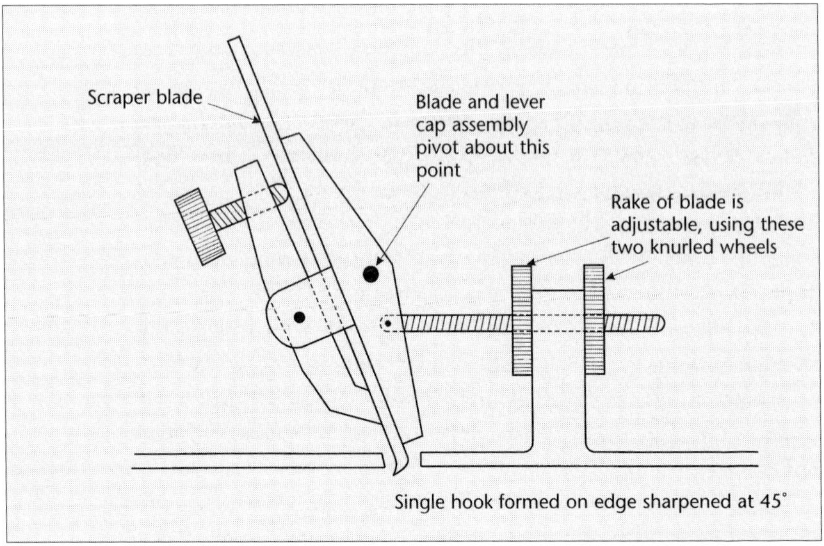

Fig 16.4 Scraper plane blade assembly.

thicker than a cabinet scraper, and is sharpened differently. It is usual to sharpen both ends of the blade: when one end becomes blunt the cutter is turned round and the other sharp end is used. The blade is put in the vice with the edge to be sharpened at the top. A bevel of about 45° is filed on it. Take care that the edge is kept straight. The filed surface is honed to remove all file marks. A ticketer is used to turn a hook on the sharp corner of the scraper blade. As with the cabinet scraper, a large hook is not as effective as a properly formed small one. Four passes of the ticketer with moderate pressure are better than two heavy passes. The rake of the blade in the scraper plane is adjustable, and some experimenting is necessary to get the best rake because the rake is dependent on the angle of the hook put on the blade (Fig 16.4). There is also a tool resembling a metal spokeshave that has a scraper blade, but it has no provision to alter the pitch.

Shaped cabinet scraper blades used on moulding and shaped surfaces are sharpened in a similar way to the straight version, though more care is needed when forming the hook. Keeping the ticketer at a constant angle while it is travelling around a shaped edge is not easy.

Square-edged Scrapers

When restoring furniture the old surface finish often has to be removed, and the best tool to use for this task is a square-edged scraper. Some craftsmen use a cabinet scraper prepared as normal but without the hook. Hence the name 'square edged'. The hook on a cabinet scraper would be blunted in a single pass over old varnish or polish, but a scraper made from a worn-out hacksaw machine blade is ideal. Engineering workshops use blades as wide as 1½in (38mm). These are made from high-speed steel, and the only way to cut them to the required length is on the corner of a grinding wheel. The edge is sharpened by grinding it square. Two working edges can be formed after the teeth are ground away. This scraper can only be sharpened on the grinding machine.

It is possible to make a handle to hold the square-edged scraper, which is a boon if there is much work to be done. Scrapers without a handle are hard on the hands. Millers' Falls Tool Company made a very useful scraper, fitted with a handle that has a ball joint in it. The handle can be put at any angle to the blade and locked there.

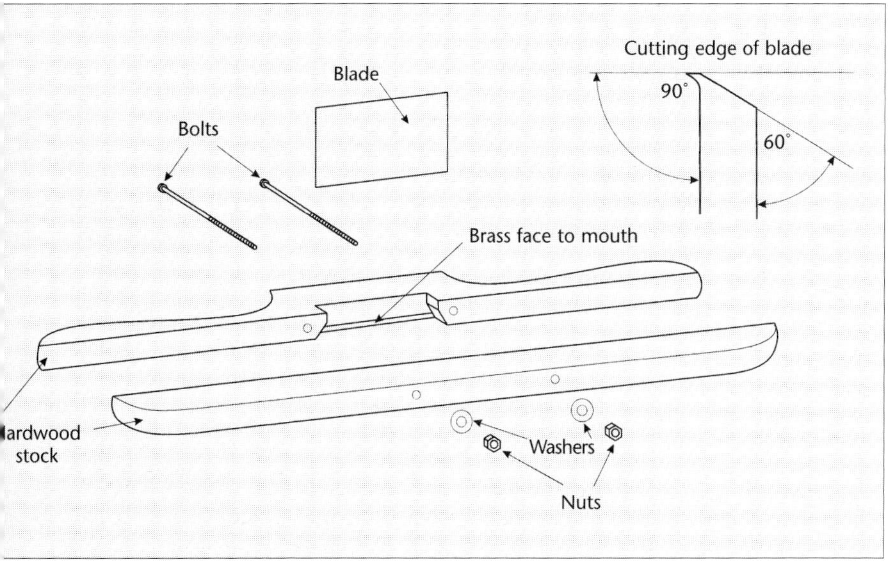

Fig 16.5 Chairmaker's scraper.

Chairmaker's Scraper

Because of the complex shape of many of the components in a chair, makers construct a scraper sometimes known as a 'chairmaker's devil'. This comprises a scraper blade, sharpened in the customary way, held between two pieces of wood, and resembles a spokeshave (Fig 16.5). The blade is prepared in exactly the same way as the scraper planes.

Skarsten Scraper

This tool is also known as a 'hooked scraper'. The Swedish firm Skarsten are the sole manufacturers, but the tool is freely available from most good toolshops. The tool comprises a handle and a separate hooked blade. The blades are disposable, but before becoming worn out they can be sharpened a number of times. The metal is soft enough to be filed. When sharpening maintain the original bevel. Various cutters are available: straight, concave, convex; or serrated for coarse work such as removing old surface finishes. Several differently shaped handles are available.

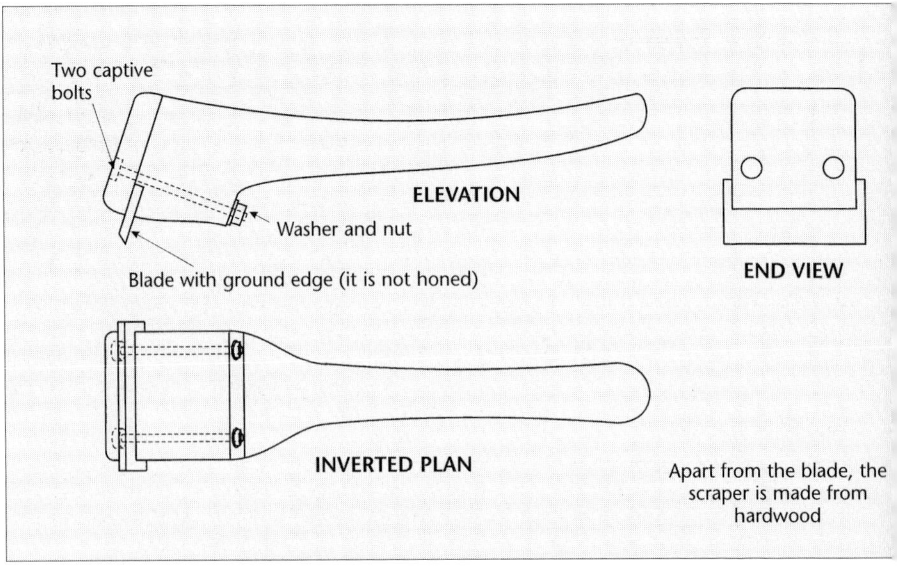

Fig 16.6 Bench or glue scraper.

Glue Scrapers

You can make a glue scraper by screwing an old worn-out plane iron to a wooden handle (Fig 16.6). The tool is used for removing the hard surplus glue that has been squeezed from a joint on to the surface of the work, and is also useful for cleaning hard glue from the surface of the bench. The edge of the tool is best left blunt. If it is sharpened there is the danger that it will cut the surface of the work when being used.

Scratch Stocks

While the scratch stock cannot truly be described as a scraper, it cuts a mould or a groove by scraping. The scratch stock is workshop made, often for a particular job. It is usually just an oddment of wood cut into a pistol shape with a blade held in a saw cut (Fig 16.7). The blades are made from broken band saw or hacksaw blades. The cutting end of the blade is a square-edged scraper. The tool cuts on both the push and pull stroke.

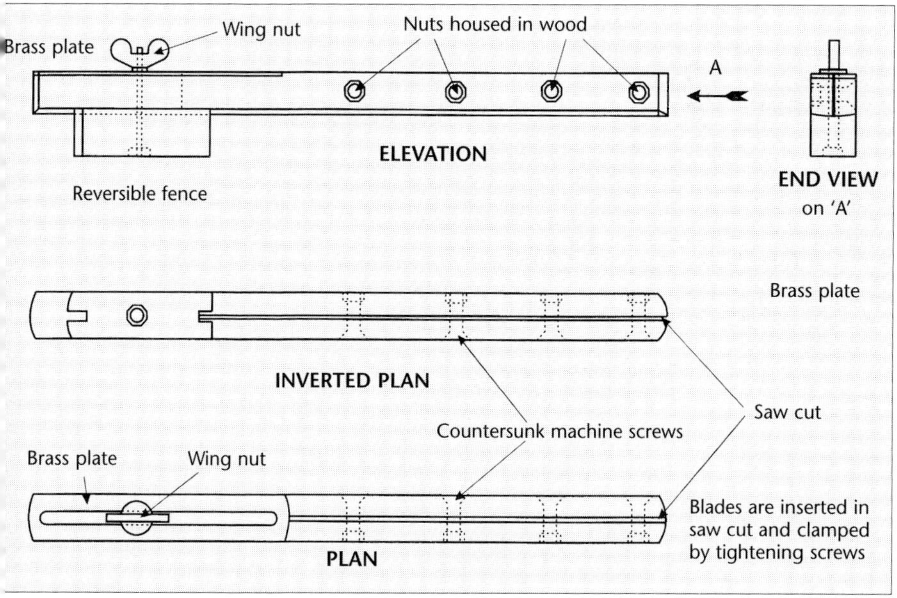

Fig 16.7 Scratch stock.

CHAPTER 17

Axes, Adzes and Froes

Axes are classified in a number of ways: the weight of the head, the tasks they are designed to perform and the way they are sharpened. The head weight is specified in pounds. The use is described simply, such as felling, cooper's, chairmaker's, mortising.

There are two distinctly different cutting edges. The axe used for normal chopping operations is sharpened with bevels on both sides (Fig 17.1). The side axe is sharpened from one side, that is to say, there is a bevel on only one side of the blade, the other side being flat (Fig 17.2). Side axes are made left or right handed, depending on which side of the blade the bevel is.

The smaller and lighter heads can be ground on the small machines used for chisel and plane irons. However, the larger-sized tools are difficult to present accurately to a small wheel. The old fashioned sandstone wheel is the ideal tool for this task. The larger-

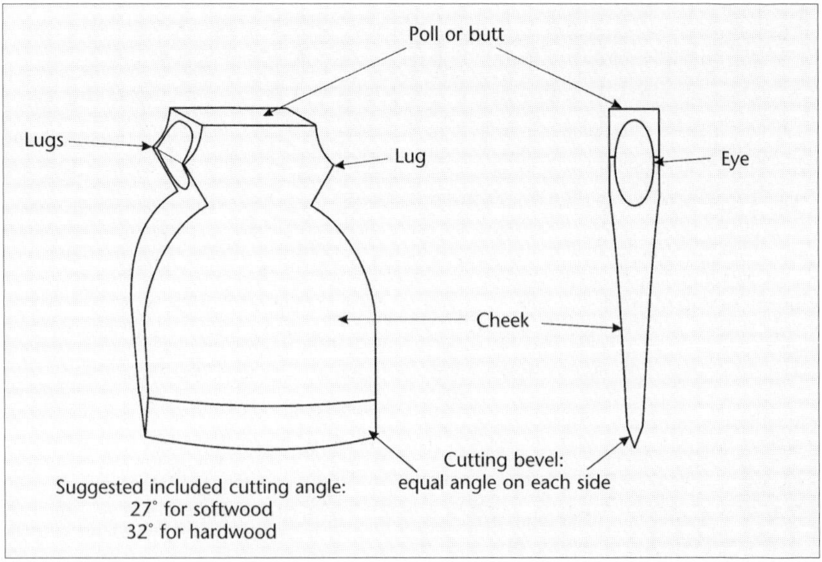

Fig 17.1 Kent axe head.

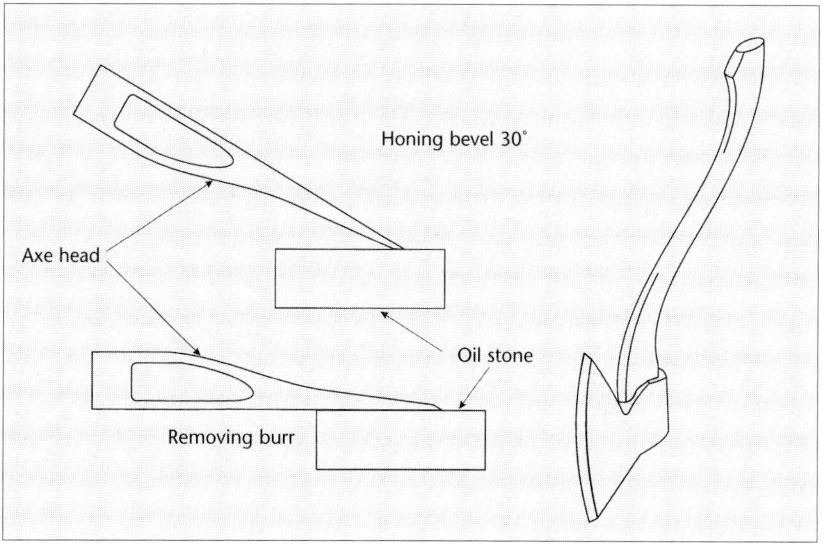

Fig 17.2 Right handed side axe.

diameter wheel also enables a flatter bevel to be ground. The axe used for normal chopping has a bevel on both sides, and the sides of the head, called the cheeks, form a wedge shape. The steeper the sides of this wedge, the more difficulty there is in driving the tool into the wood, particularly in a cross-grain cut. The tool works best with a very narrow honing bevel. As this is made larger every time the tool is honed there will be a need to regrind the cheeks. The included grinding angle for workshop axes should be between 20° and 25°. The side axe, which is used in a different fashion, is ground at 25°.

The shape of the cutting edge on the axe head is determined by the work the tool is used for and the preference of the user. A slight curve is usual, but a straight edge on a small side axe can be very useful. Honing is carried out by placing the head flat on the bench with the edge to be honed projecting over the bench edge (Fig 17.3). Hold the head firmly, and rub an oil stone flat on the honing bevel. It is easiest if only the end of the stone is used, leaving the other end to be gripped in the hand. Move the oil stone in a circular movement. Treat both sides equally and work along the full length of the cutting edge.

The side axe has the bevel honed in a similar fashion from one

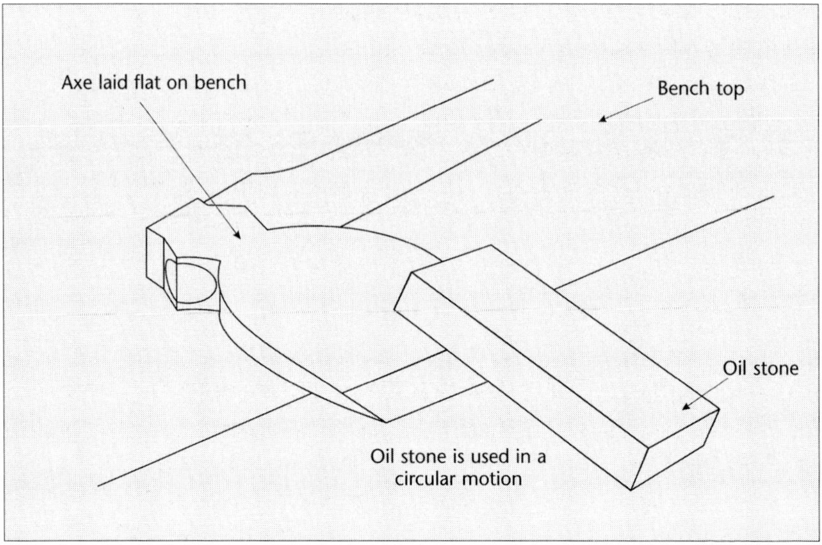

Fig 17.3 Honing an axe on the bench.

side. The small heads are best held in the hand and the flat side rubbed on a stationary stone. The larger heads are placed in a similar position as used to hone the bevel. The stone must be kept flat on the surface. Be very careful not to lose the flat face, which must continue right to the cutting edge.

Adzes

The adze has a curved blade, and the part that forms the handle socket is in line with the grinding bevel. This makes most adze heads difficult to grind, and the side of the wheel usually has to be used. The adze has a bevel on the inside of the blade, and the outside is flat (Fig 17.4). The inside is honed by placing the tool's head on the bench in a similar way to that described for the axe. The outside needs special attention, because the blade is curved right up to the cutting edge. This curve must be maintained. Because of the way the head is fitted to the handle, it can be removed for sharpening, which makes for much easier positioning while both grinding and honing. Many small hand adzes have their handles fitted similar to the method used for hammers, and these are not removable for sharpening. Some small hand adzes used to rough-shape carvings have very curved blades, that is, they take a scooped cut. It is impossible to hone these with a flat stone. Slip stones tend to be too small and if used produce a misshapen edge. An old hone is usually rubbed to the shape of the adze blade and reserved just for that tool. Rubbing a hard Carborundum or Arkansas stone to shape is a very arduous task, but a Japanese water stone is soft and easily makes the shape required.

Froes

The blade of a froe is usually from 6in (152mm) to 12in (305mm) long and wedge shaped in section, and has a round socket at one end to receive the handle (Fig 17.5). The froe is used to split (rive) wood. There are two advantages in riving rather than sawing timber. It is much quicker, and the resultant piece of wood has the grain running parallel to the surface throughout its length. This is

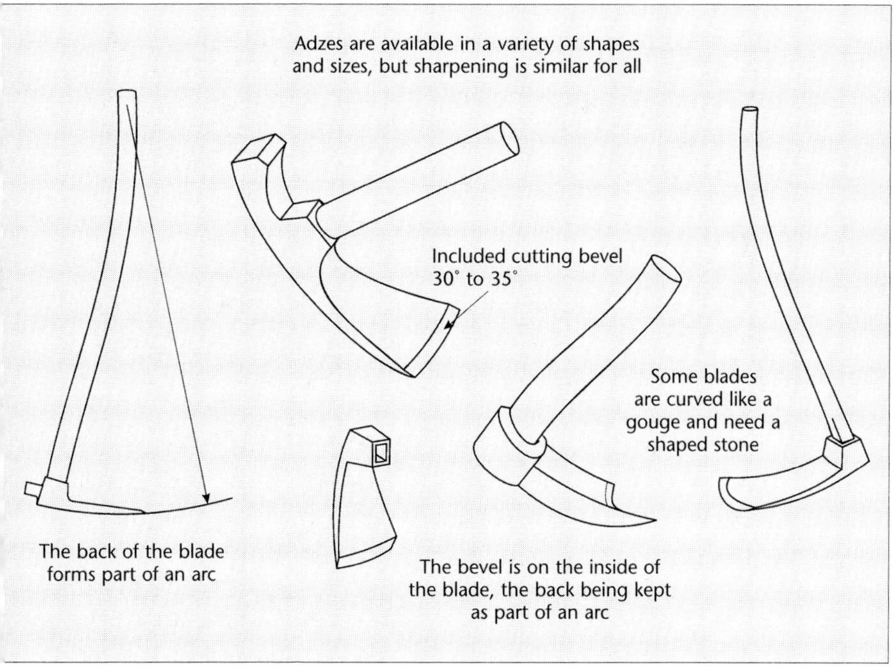

Fig 17.4 The adze.

particularly important in stressed items like the spokes of a wheel or the treenails (pronounced 'trenels') used in wooden ship building. The edge of the froe should not be too sharp or it will tend to cut the wood rather than split it. The edge is produced by using a coarse stone. There is never a need to grind the tool.

The lathmaker's froe has a large, flat blade, which is sharpened on the end as well as on the long edge. While the froe should be driven with a wooden club, it is not unusual to find a second-hand example that has the back burred through being hit with a hammer. If the damage is not too severe the burr can be ground away.

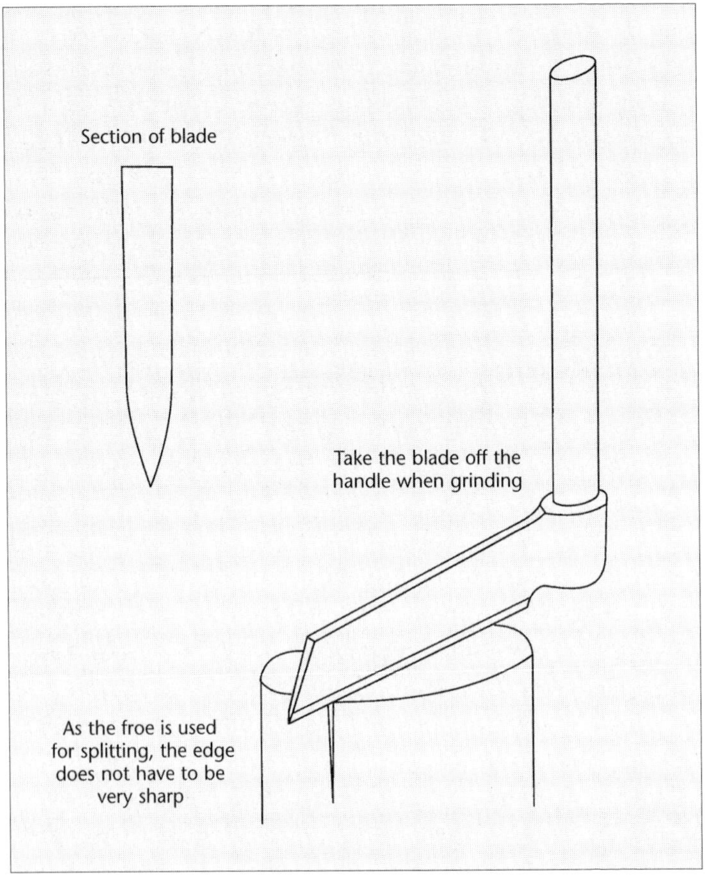

Fig 17.5 The froe.

CHAPTER 18

Knives

Marking-out Knives

The marking-out knife, sometimes referred to as a striking knife, comes in several patterns. One style has the end of the blade at an angle of 45° to the length of the blade. Another has two angles meeting at a point. A third type has a knife at one end of the blade and a marking awl at the other – this is not recommended, as the sharp point of the awl is too near the eyes when you get close to position the knife accurately. All striking knives should be sharpened with a bevel on one side only. The flat face of the blade fits tight against the blade of a square or the end of a rule. If there is a bevel on both sides the bevel is inclined to keep the cutting edge away from the square. Which shape to use is probably one of personal preference. I make my own from old machine hacksaw blades (Fig 18.1). The part of the blade that does 90% of the work is the very tip, so this part receives most

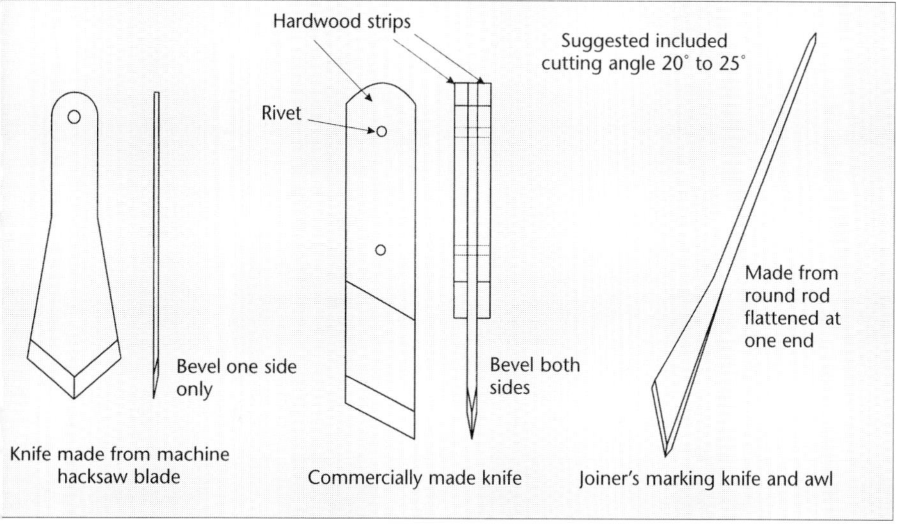

Fig 18.1 Marking or striking knives.

attention when sharpening. As the blades of my marking knives are on the thin side I only use a single sharpening bevel of about 20°. Thick blades, like those on shop-bought examples, need to have a grinding angle or honing will take too long. If the blade is the type with the end shaped at two angles it can be used either left or right handed. The variety with a single angle is right handed. Some woodworkers have a pair: one left hand and one right hand.

Japanese marking knives are also available. These are beautiful tools with a laminated blade, coming complete with wooden scabbard (Fig 18.2). The edge is sharpened with a single bevel. The blade is thick, but because only the very face is hard steel the soft backing metal is soon removed when honing.

Whittling and Carving Knives

These are used to make items such as cupboard door pulls and other small fittings. The finest starting point is an old cut-throat razor. These are made of steel that takes a supreme cutting edge. My carving knives have small blades, as these are easy to control. The blade is initially shaped on a grinding machine, but the fine finishing is done on a Japanese water stone.

Knives used for this sort of work need thin cutting edges. The blade is ground so that the sides have an included angle as small as 15°. The cutting edge is formed by two very narrow honed bevels at

Fig 18.2 Japanese marking knife.

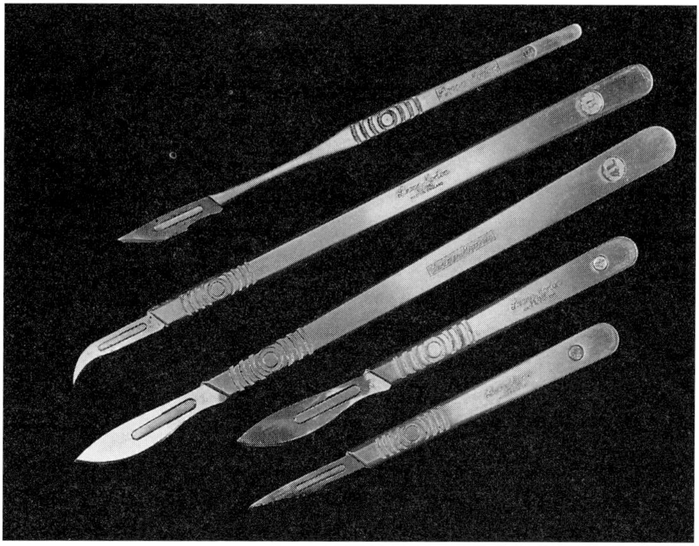

Fig 18.3 Various patterns of Swann-Morton scalpels.

30° to one another. These bevels are so narrow that they are difficult to see. When honing these knives, pass the blade along the stone with the edge trailing. Lift the knife and return it to the end of the stone and take another trailing pass. Keep both sides of the blade equal.

Scalpels

Modern scalpels with disposable blades are useful items in any workshop, and are used for all sorts of fine cutting work. There are two sizes of blade and several designs of both blade and handle. The most popular are those made by Swann-Morton (Fig 18.3). The nickel handles work very well. There are also several handles made by other manufacturers that still use the Swann-Morton blades, though the only one of these that is worth mentioning is the Ernie Ives marquetry pattern (Fig 18.4). This tool looks like a fountain pen. The blade is held firmly and only the very tip is exposed, which ensures that the blade is held rigid. This tool cuts marquetry veneer very accurately. Although the blades are expendable it is still possible to sharpen them. In fact, for marquetry cutting where only the very tip is used, sharpening is to

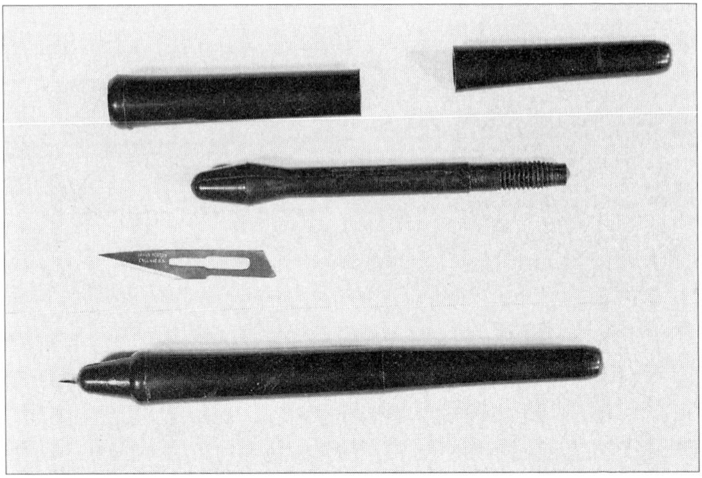

Fig 18.4 Ernie Ives marquetry scalpel.

be recommended. This thins the point and the cutting action of the sharpened blade is better than when new. The blades are installed in a handle for sharpening (the Swann-Morton handle number 3 is ideal for this purpose) as they are so small it is impossible to hold them accurately without the handle. Drag the blade along the stone with the edge trailing. Repeat this stroke several times on each side of the blade. By concentrating on the point it is possible to thin the blade in this area.

Hacking Knives

Re-glazing doors and windows is a common task, and varies from working on a sash window to delicate bookcase doors with astragal bars. Removing the hard putty needs a sharpish tool, but it spoils the edge of any tool that is used. The hardened steel in a chisel blade will chip if exposed to this rough treatment. A hacking knife is the tool made especially for this purpose (Fig 18.5). The blade is formed from a steel suitable for the task. There is no point in sharpening this tool so that it will cut wood – in fact, if it is too sharp it is difficult to remove the hard putty without damaging the wood. Ground bevels are quite sufficient. Even so, the edge needs frequent attention if the tool is to work efficiently.

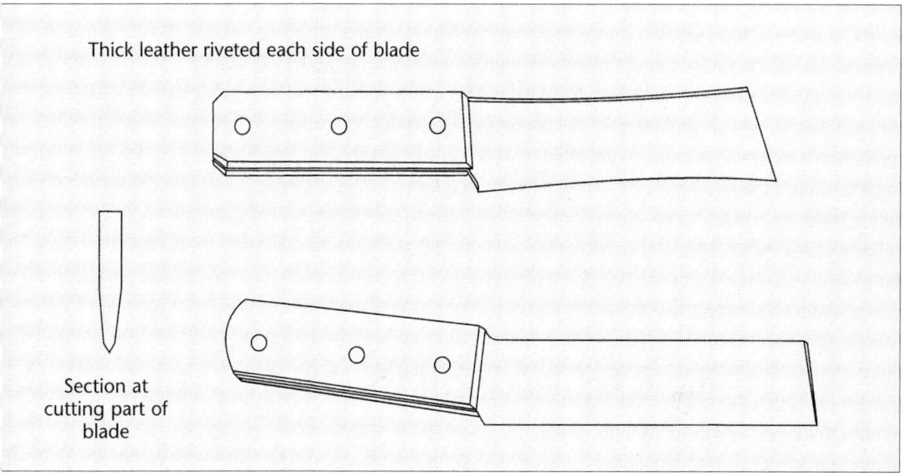

Fig 18.5 Hacking knives.

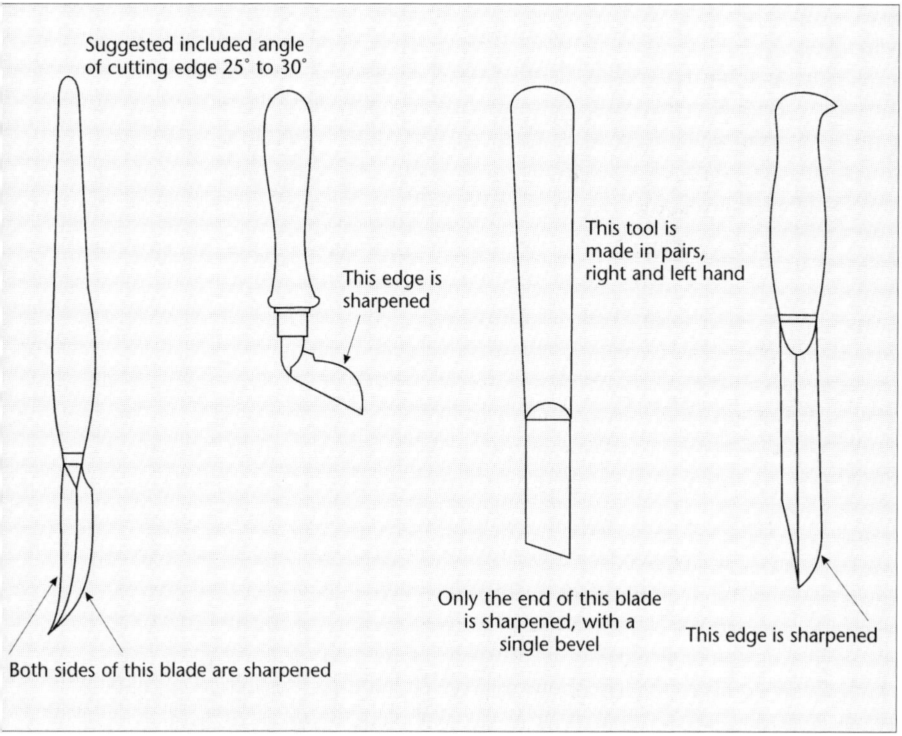

Fig 18.6 Chip-carving knives.

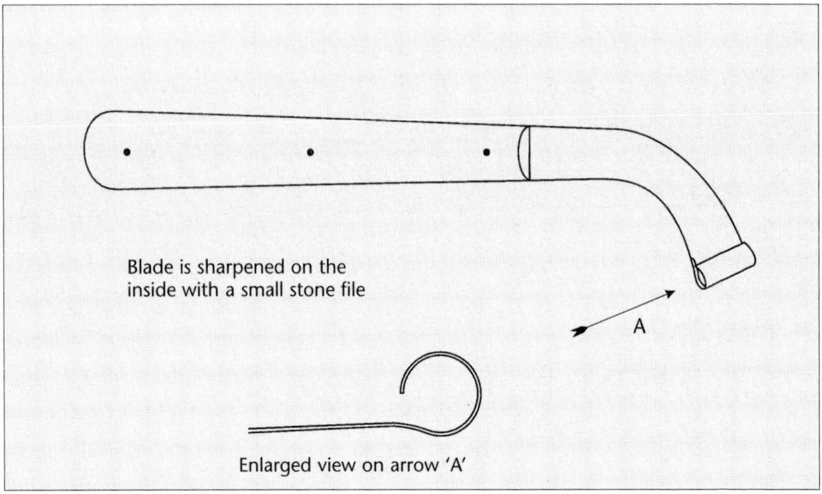

Fig 18.7 Scriving knife.

Gilding Knives

The long-bladed knife used to cut gold leaf is another tool that is not given a truly sharp edge. If a keen edge were put on the tool it would cut the guilder's cushion. Gilding knives do not normally need sharpening.

Chip-carving Knives

A number of different-shaped knives are used for chip carving, most having the blade sharpened on its end (Fig 18.6). The end can be at 90° or at a sloping angle, which gives the tools a chisel-like appearance. However, they are not sharpened like a chisel. The edge is formed by a bevel on both sides of the blade. The knife is used in a stabbing action. Some workers like a single bevel, that is to say, there is no separate grinding and honing angle. The included angle of the cutting edge is 30°. A shallower angle than this can be used on softwood, but an angle less than 27° will not give an edge that lasts long. Other shaped knives are used for cutting curved chips, and come in a variety of shapes. The edge is formed similarly to that on a whittling knife.

Scriving Knives

The scriving knife is also known as the 'timber scribe'. This tool is used to inscribe numbers or special marks on timber, and is used mainly in the timber trade. The blade has the end bent round to form a gouge-like cutter (Fig 18.7). The inside of this curve is sharpened with a slip stone, maintaining the original bevel. Shipwrights use a similar tool which they call a 'scrive hook'.

Bench Knives

Bench knives are made by the craftsman for his own use, and consist of two flat pieces of steel ¾in (19mm) wide and 1in (25mm) long, sharpened along one long edge (Fig 18.8). They are used to hold small lengths of wood to the bench when working rebates and mouldings (though the practice is frowned on by some as it eventually spoils the bench top). These tools are often made from old table-knife blades. If they are made from thin steel they do not have to be very sharp. After the initial sharpening when they were made they are not normally resharpened.

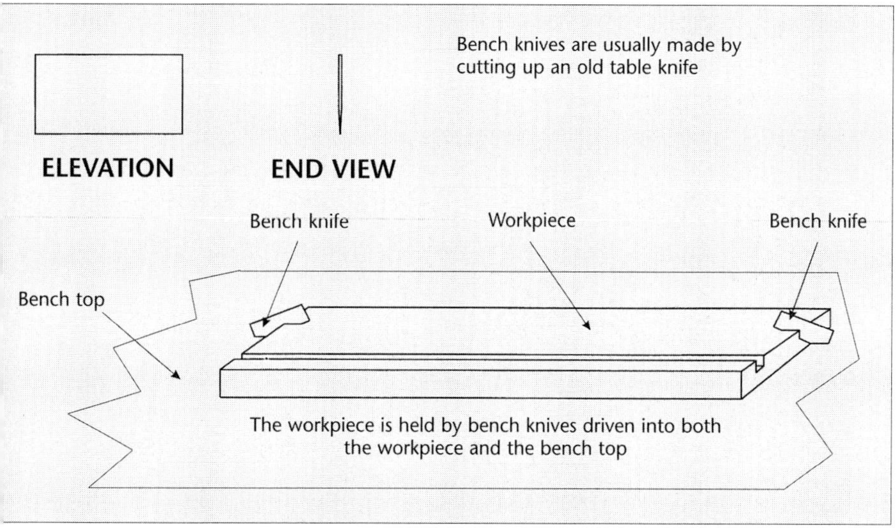

Fig 18.8 Bench knives.

CHAPTER 19

Draw Knives and Spokeshaves

Flat Straight Draw Knives

Draw knives are so named because they are drawn towards the user. Although there are many different patterns, the straight variety are all sharpened in the same way. The blade can be from 6in (152mm) to 18in (457mm) long. The centre of the blade does most of the work, and thus is the part to first become blunt. There is a tendency just to sharpen the blunt part, but this leads to the cutting edge becoming curved in length and makes the tool difficult to use. It is

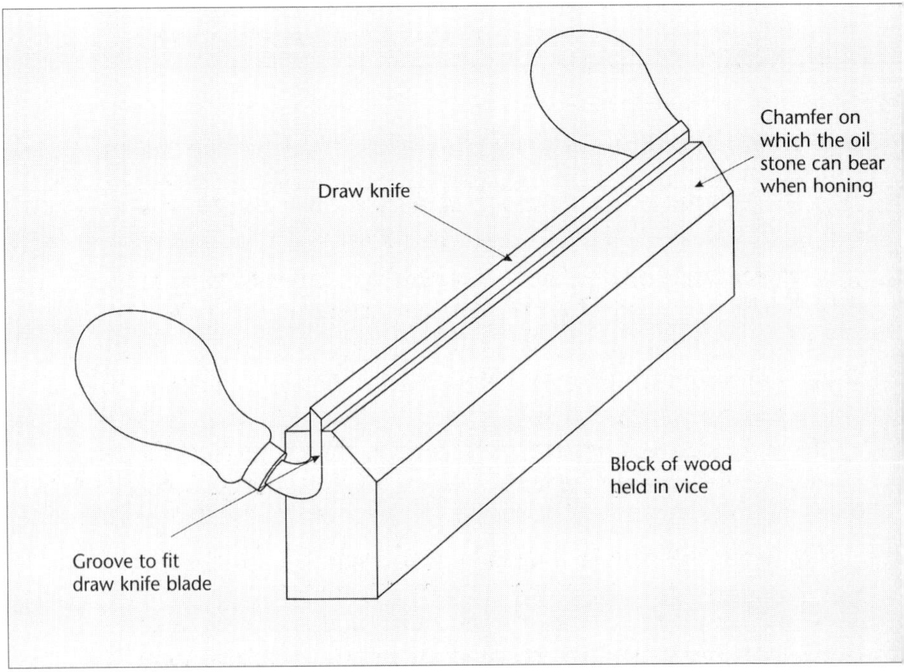

Fig 19.1 Honing a draw knife.

essential that the full length of the blade is treated the same.

The tool is sharpened with a bevel on only one side of the blade, and for most work a cutting edge made by an angle of 30° will be found suitable. When grinding the tool at 5° less than the cutting angle, care must be taken to keep the bevel straight and even throughout the entire length of the blade. A jig is needed to hold the tool while honing, made from a piece of wood the same length as the blade, with a groove worked in one edge (Fig 19.1). The groove's width is made so that the blade fits snugly into it. The depth of the groove is made so that the part of the blade protruding allows free passage of the hone along the bevel. The jig is held in the vice and the stone rubbed from end to end of the draw knife's blade. Be very cautious when doing this, it is very easy to cut yourself. Once the edge is to your satisfaction remove the tool from the jig and rub the blade flat, face down on the stone, to remove any burr. A tool with a concave shape in the length of the cutting edge through uneven sharpening is a nuisance, but a blade that has a convex edge is preferred for some tasks. As with the straight blade, this shape must be maintained during sharpening, which is carried out in a similar fashion.

Curved-blade Draw Knives

A number of hand crafts use draw knives that have curved blades. Coopers use a number of these, usually referred to as 'inshaves' or 'scorpers'. There is also the circular heading knife and the jigger. Windsor chair makers use a scorp to shape the surface of the chair's seat. Sharpening these curved tools is not easy. The bevel on the heading knife and the jigger is on the inside of the curve, and a stone with a slightly rounded face is used to service these tools. All the other tools in this group are sharpened with the bevel on the outside of the curve. The tool is held on the bench top with one hand, with part of the blade overhanging the edge of the bench. This part is honed with the stone held in the other hand. The tool is repositioned to bring a different part over the bench edge to be honed. This procedure is continued until all of the bevel has been honed. It may be necessary to use a large slip stone inside the curve to remove any burr.

Wooden Spokeshaves

The wooden spokeshave consists of a stock usually made from box or beech some 4–16in (102–406mm) long. The ends of the stock are shaped to form handles. The cutter is wedge shaped and 1½in (38mm) to 5in (127mm) long. There are two tapered square tangs, one at each end of the cutter. The cutter has a single bevel on its top surface, and the lower surface is flat. There is a difficulty in sharpening the cutter. The two tangs preclude rubbing the bevel flat on a stone, so a stone narrower than the distance between the tangs must be used. The normal procedure is to stand a bench stone on its edge. The blade can then be rubbed on the top edge of the stone (Fig 19.2). Because of the width of the stone the tangs can hang down either side and not be fouled by the bench. Keeping the inside bevel flat is difficult, and it tends to become hollow in the centre. If this happens the shaving removed at the centre is usually coarser than that at the sides. If a cutter becomes hollow it can usually be

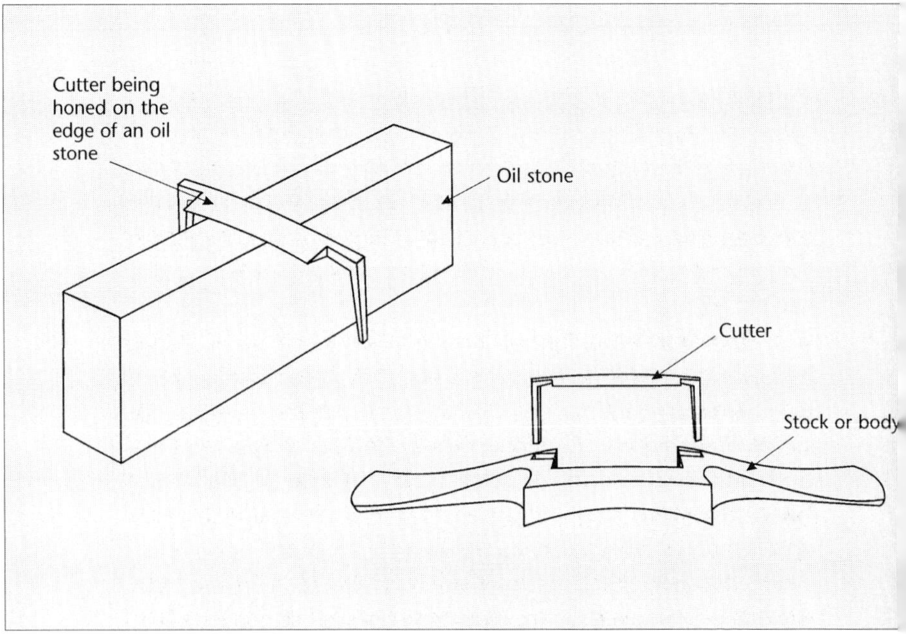

Fig 19.2 Honing the cutter of a wooden spokeshave.

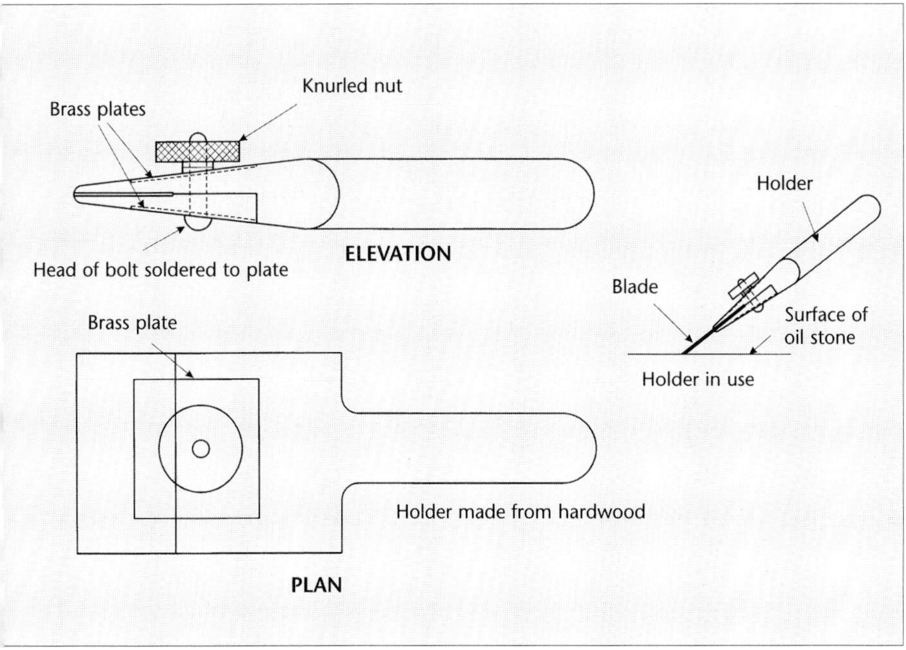

Fig 19.3 Holder for the blades of a metal spokeshave.

corrected on a grinding wheel. The outside of the blade is rubbed flat on the stone. It might be found that the under face has a gentle curve from end to end. Be careful to maintain this curve.

Replacement blades are obtainable, though fitting one requires some ingenuity. The tangs are often of a different size from those of the original blade and some packing or remodelling of the tang holes is necessary.

There is a very small amount of sole bearing on the workpiece when the shave is being used. This part of the stock wears hollow, so the spokeshave may become useless. However, a piece of brass can be inlaid into the sole of the stock, which usually produces a tool that performs better than new. A superior form of wooden spokeshave blade has threaded tangs fitted with wing nuts. This simplifies setting up the tool. Occasionally one comes across the 'radius spokeshave', a tool no longer made, with a curved blade that has to be sharpened with a slip stone. Several different metal spokeshaves have replaced this tool.

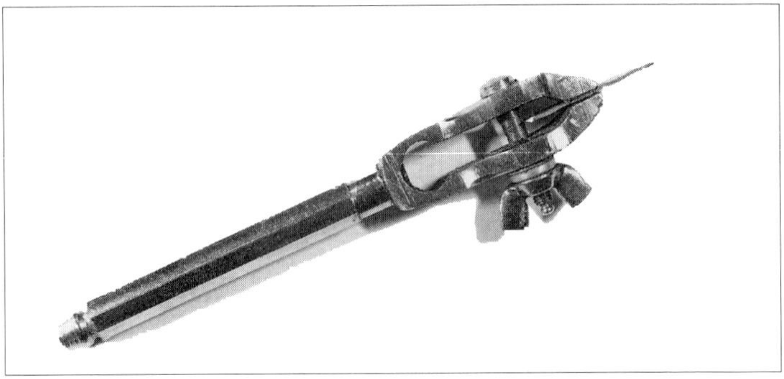

Fig 19.4 A jeweller's hand vice, holding a small blade for honing.

Metal Spokeshaves

There are many different types and patterns of metal spokeshave. The most common type comes in two versions: flat sole and rounded sole. The blades are identical in both. The blades are difficult to hold, so a device must be made in which to hold them (Fig 19.3). Apart from the problem of holding the blade they are sharpened in a

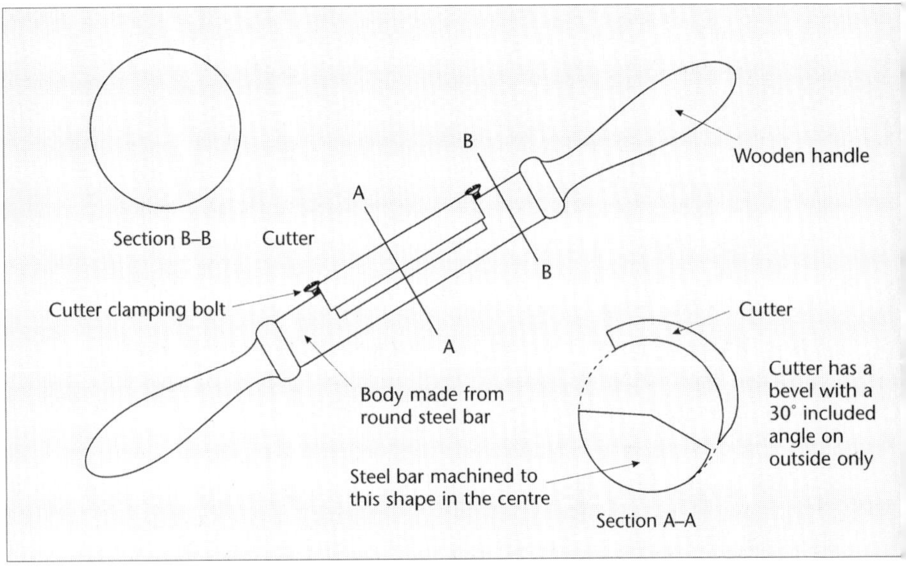

Fig 19.5 Circular spokeshave.

similar fashion to plane irons (Chapter 8). If you have trouble with the tool chattering when you use it, see if the blade is bedding flat in the stock of the tool. This is a common problem with many modern tools. It is a long job filing the bed to mate with the blade, but it is the only way to cure the problem. The best and sweetest working metal spokeshaves I have are made by Prestons, and are the only pattern I know of with a lateral adjuster.

Metal spokeshaves are also made with round or hollow cutters. The round is easily sharpened, using the holder described above. The blade is rolled as it is honed so that all of the cutting edge is equally honed. It is important that the cutting edge maintains the same shape as the sole of the stock. During sharpening it is necessary to assemble the cutter in the stock and check this from time to time. The hollow cutters are similar to those of a hollow moulding plane, which means that a shaped stone has to be used to hone the bevel.

Miniature Spokeshaves

The very small spokeshaves prized by pattern and model makers are just miniature versions of the full-size tools. Some craftsmen have a number of these tools with various shaped soles. It may be necessary to make a special small version of the blade holder to sharpen the cutters. The most convenient tool for this is a jeweller's hand vice (Fig 19.4).

Circular Spokeshave

The circular spokeshave is an unconventional tool. The stock consists of a casting circular in section, and the blade is of semi-tubular section sharpened with a bevel on the outside. The cutter is clamped by two screws. This tool is used on very small internal radii where no other tool will cut. It is not an easy tool to use, made worse if it is not sharpened correctly. The cutting angle is shown in Fig 19.5. On no account remove metal from the inside of the cutter.

Circular Routers

The circular router is also known as the 'quirk router'. The cutter of this tool takes the form of two hooked teeth facing one another. One tooth has an inverted 'V' section. The points of the 'V' form two sharp spurs that cut the side of a groove. The other tooth has a sharp cutting edge and removes a shaving from between the cuts made by the spurs (Fig 19.6). The tool is supplied with a number of different-thickness cutters that work grooves of various widths. Every time a cutter is sharpened metal is removed from it. There is very little spare metal, so sharpening should be undertaken with care. Sharpening is carried out by removing metal from the inside of the teeth, and a round stone file made from fine-grade grit is the best tool for this task. A rub on the underside of the cutting blade with a flat stone will remove any burr.

Other Routers of Spokeshave Form

A number of tools resemble a metal spokeshave, except they have a shaped sole and cutter. These are used for working beads and mouldings on circular work. Most have two cutters, one being a mirror image of the other, so the tool can always be used in a direction where it is not cutting into end grain. Sharpening follows the procedure described in Chapter 8 for sharpening moulding planes.

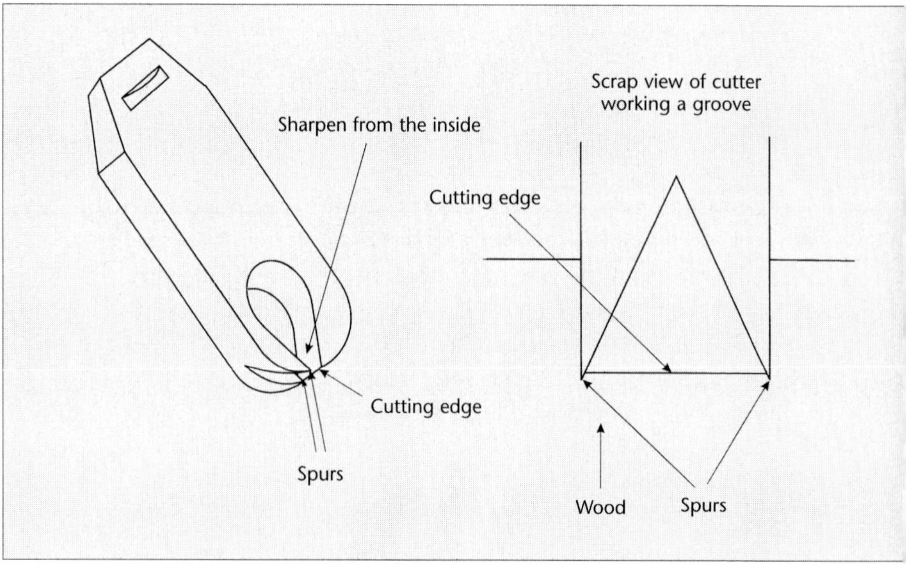

Fig 19.6 Circular router cutter.

Acknowledgements

I should like to express my grateful thanks to my wife Jo, who corrected my spelling and generally put up with my deafness while I was fighting the word processor.

I am indebted to the editorial staff at the Guild of Master Craftsmen, who encouraged me, and were always there at the end of the phone when I needed someone to talk to.

It would not be possible to write subjectively about different sharpening surfaces without being able to test and evaluate them. My thanks, therefore, also go to the following: Mr Richard Starkie of Starkie and Starkie Ltd who supplied the DMT diamond sharpening devices; Chesterman Marketing Ltd, who supplied the ceramic sharpening stones; Mr Paul Brown of Craftsman's Choice, who supplied Japanese tools and water stones.

Bibliography

Corkhill, T., *A Glossary of Wood*, Stobart & Son, London, 1979.

Emary, A. B., *Site Carpentry and Advanced Joinery*, Macmillan, Basingstoke, 1985.

Feirer, J. L., *Advanced Woodwork and Furniture Making*, Chas A. Bennet, Peoria, IL, 1978.

George, M., *Metalworking: A Manual of Techniques*, Crowood Press, Swindon, 1991.

Hayward, C. H., *Tools for Woodwork*, Evans, London, 1975.

Joyce, E., *The Technique of Furniture Making*, Batsford, London, 1980.

Mersirow, K. and Herman, R., *The Care and Use of Japanese Woodworking Tools*, Woburn, MA, 1978.

Odate, T., *Japanese Woodworking Tools*, Taunton Press, Newtown, CT, 1984.

Salaman, R. A., *Dictionary of Tools*, Allen & Unwin, London, 1975.

Sherlock, F. E., *Machine Woodworking Technology*, Newnes-Butterworth, London, 1973.

Simmonds, A., *Wide Band Saws*, Stobart & Son, London, 1980.

Taylor, V., *The Woodworker Dictionary*, Argus, Hemel Hempstead, 1987.

Voisey, N. S., *Wood Machining*, Stobart & Son, London, 1987.

Fine Woodworking on planes and chisels, Taunton Press, Newtown, CT.

Metric conversion table

inches to millimetres and centimetres
mm = millimetres cm = centimetres

inches	mm	cm	inches	cm	inches	cm
⅛	3	0.3	9	22.9	30	76.2
¼	6	0.6	10	25.4	31	78.7
⅜	10	1.0	11	27.9	32	81.3
½	13	1.3	12	30.5	33	83.8
⅝	16	1.6	13	33.0	34	86.4
¾	19	1.9	14	35.6	35	88.9
⅞	22	2.2	15	38.1	36	91.4
1	25	2.5	16	40.6	37	94.0
1¼	32	3.2	17	43.2	38	96.5
1½	38	3.8	18	45.7	39	99.1
1¾	44	4.4	19	48.3	40	101.6
2	51	5.1	20	50.8	41	104.1
2½	64	6.4	21	53.3	42	106.7
3	76	7.6	22	55.9	43	109.2
3½	89	8.9	23	58.4	44	111.8
4	102	10.2	24	61.0	45	114.3
4½	114	11.4	25	63.5	46	116.8
5	127	12.7	26	66.0	47	119.4
6	152	15.2	27	68.6	48	121.9
7	178	17.8	28	71.1	49	124.5
8	203	20.3	29	73.7	50	127.0

About the Author

Jim Kingshott is a professional cabinetmaker who served his apprenticeship in the late 1940s, and, in more recent years, has been involved in the training of apprentices. He has been a regular freelance contributor to woodworking magazines for a number of years, and is the author of three books: *Making and Modifying Woodworking Tools* (1992), *The Workshop* (1993) and *Sharpening: The Complete Guide* (1994), all published by GMC Publications.

Index

TITLES AVAILABLE FROM GMC PUBLICATIONS